Forests of Hope

Translated by Theodore Wachs

with assistance from

Thomas Kohler,
Centre for Development and Environment,
University of Berne, Switzerland,

and

Margaret J Sieber, Birmensdorf, Switzerland

Canadian Cataloguing in Publication Data:
A catalog record for this publication is available from the National Library of Canada and the Library of Congress.

Cover design by Dominic Banner: photo by Christian Küchli
Typesetting by PCS Mapping & DTP, Newcastle upon Tyne, UK
Printed by Mateu Cromo, Spain

Inquiries regarding requests to reprint all or part of *Forests of Hope* should be addressed to New Society Publishers at the address below.

ISBN: 1 86571 378 2

To order directly from the publishers, please add $3.50 to the price of the first copy, and $1.00 for each additional copy (plus GST in Canada). Send check or money order to:

New Society Publishers
P.O. Box 189, Gabriola Island, BC V0R 1X0, Canada

New Society Publishers aims to publish books for fundamental social change through nonviolent action. We focus especially on sustainable living, progressive leadership, and educational and parenting resources. Our full list of books can be browsed on the world wide web at:
http://www.newsociety.com

NEW SOCIETY PUBLISHERS
Gabriola Island, BC, Canada and Stony Creek, CT, USA

Contents

To Ian Hutchinson

*The only forester I ever met in the
tropics who would even take a bus
to reach the forest.*

Acknowledgements

The author and the publisher wish to express their thanks to the following institutions and enterprises for their support during the preparation of *Forests of Hope*.

The Avina Foundation, Hurden, Switzerland
Federal Office of Environment, Forests and Landscape, Berne, Switzerland
Federal Office for Foreign Economic Affairs, Berne, Switzerland
Ciba-Geigy AG, Basel, Switzerland
The Deutsche Gesellschaft für Technische Zusammenarbeit, Eschborn, Germany
Swiss Development Corporation (SDC), Berne, Switzerland
Intercooperation, Berne, Switzerland
The Johann Jacobs Foundation, Zurich, Switzerland
The Migros Co-operative Association, Zurich, Switzerland
The Seva Lottery Fund of the Canton of Berne, Switzerland
The Karl Mayer Foundation, Triesen, Liechtenstein
Rolex SA, Biel/Bienne, Switzerland
The Swiss Forestry Society, Zurich, Switzerland
The City of Biel/Bienne, Switzerland
The World Wide Fund for Nature, Zurich, Switzerland

The author also wishes to thank the many people in the different countries he visited who supported and encouraged him and also offered helpful comments. Particular thanks go to the following individuals:

Pichai Assavavipas, Sylvia Bahri, Sunderlal Bahuguna, Dominique Bauwens, H.S. Bishnoi, Keith S. Brown, Jr., Gerardo Budowski, Dietrich Burger, Jane Carter, Mario Dantas, Manfred Denich, Pidet Dolarom, Laure Emperaire, Philip Fearnside, Gomercindo Garcia Rodrigues, Nancy Glover, Don Gilmour, Ruedi Hager, Ian Hutchinson,[†] Bill Jackson, Jean-Paul Jeanrenaud, Fred Kabare, Gerald Kapp, Ludwig Karner, Masakazu Kashio, Alexander Kastl, Luan Shen Qiang, Tej Mahat, Bill Macklin, Jeffrey A. McNeely, Kimani Muhia, Lucio Pedroni, Suntisuck Prasitsak, Nick Roche, Octavio Reis Filho, Ali Sadeli, Horst Siebert, Leonardo Sousa da Cruz, Thomas Stadtmüller, Jörg Steiner, Hansjürg Steinlin, Rolf Suelzer, Jean-Pierre Veillon, Kazumi Watanabe, Thomas Weber, Horst Weisgerber, Wang Zonghan, Yang Yuchou.

Special thanks go to Theodore Wachs, who completed the English translation with great care.

The world's forests appeared to be facing a bleak future in the early 1980s. Trees in Europe and North America were showing the effects of damage obviously due to exhaust gases produced by the burning of fossil fuels, while tropical rain forests were being submitted to the ravages of chainsaws and fire. Population growth in the Himalayas appeared to be destroying the forests that are the foundations of the 'roof of the world', thereby threatening to trigger large-scale erosion. The disappearance of trees, unquestioningly accepted as an indication of environmental degradation, evoked reactions ranging from disheartening feelings of powerlessness to various forms of cynicism.

In 1984 I had the good fortune to meet Sunderlal Bahuguna, a charismatic proponent of the Chipko Movement, which was born in the 1970s as a popular uprising against exploitation of forests in the Himalayas of India. After talking with Bahuguna, who happened to be in Europe at the time, I found myself thinking that there must be people and movements everywhere with a similar courageous dedication to preserving forests. I decided to set out on a long personal journey to test my assumption. The denuded forestland, eroded mountain slopes and landslides which I saw on my subsequent travels struck me as appropriate material for a book announcing the coming of the Day of Judgement. The brutal reality of this environmental destruction is reflected in the statistics on deforestation compiled by international organisations. But there is another reality as well: everywhere I went, I encountered men and women who treated trees and forests as resources which they could bequeath to their children largely intact. The fate of forests is determined by the context of human conflict. In the final analysis, political and economic power, ownership, and questions of incapacitation and empowerment at the local level determine whether trees will thrive or perish. Who owns the forests? Who has effective

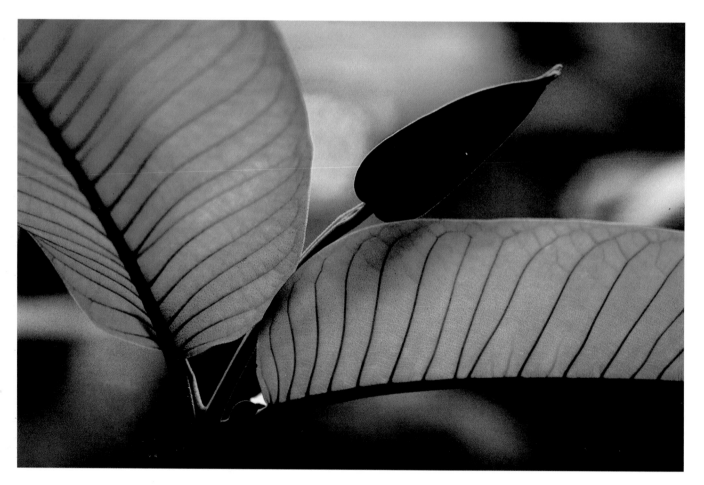

control over forest resources? Who profits from timber and other forest products? Whose interests do forestry officials and other government authorities represent?

This book attempts to confront these questions by exploring conditions in 12 different countries. Although the causes of forest degradation are complex, a basic pattern emerges everywhere: wherever national governments or powerful market forces deny local people the chance to control their own resources, profound changes in land use occur. Trees often disappear, or forests are converted to monocultures whose economic and social benefits are no greater than those offered by originally existing forms of vegetation. Despite statistics that paint a discouraging picture, I have observed developments that inspire my hope for the world's forests. In many parts of the world there is now local resistance against wanton exploitation by external forces. Groups in civil society, such as non-governmental organisations which support local people in the struggle to secure their rights, often play a decisive role in successfully opposing exploitation. Land tenure must be carefully defined, and political conditions must be stable, if the art of forest management based on near-natural principles is to be practised with any chance of realising its true potential.

The regenerative capacity shown by forest vegetation is certainly one symbol of hope. Most people have long since written off areas where irreversible degradation was thought to have occurred almost 30 years ago. Yet it is precisely in the areas where damage was worst that forest regeneration is taking place on a large scale: cut-off stems are now coppicing and new trees are sprouting up. Nevertheless, it will take decades or even centuries until these pioneer stands resemble the forests that once existed on the same sites.

Reforestation in Central Europe in the last 150 years testifies to the self-healing capacity of forest vegetation. The example of Europe also illustrates the important role of sweeping social change in promoting forest recovery. The appearance of the railway, the use of coal as a source of energy, and the coming of industrialisation in the last century helped to alleviate social disparities and greatly mitigated basic conflicts over forest resources. Far-reaching change in the countries of the South, provided that it affects all sectors of society, could now contribute decisively to the recovery of forests there as well. But the energy-intensive industrial model and the excessive patterns of consumption that have developed in the North cannot be expanded at will in a heavily populated world with rapidly dwindling resources. This makes it imperative that we develop and institute a universal culture of sustainability, in which all human beings have fair access to natural resources and the chance to earn a livelihood. The currently gloomy outlook for the world's forests will brighten in proportion to our progress on the long road towards this goal.

Christian Küchli,
May 1997

He Who Plants Trees Will Go to Heaven

Karl Kasthofer was appointed district forester in Interlaken in 1806. Conditions in Switzerland at this time were strikingly similar to conditions now found in so-called developing countries. The fundamental problem concerning forests in the early nineteenth century was one of conflicting demands at several different levels. Townspeople, and most foresters, originally saw the forest as a source of fuelwood and later as a source of timber. Farmers, on the other hand, wanted leaf fodder for their animals and litter to use in producing fertiliser. In addition, there were disputes among rural people, many of whom had no land and were therefore dependent on forest resources for their subsistence. These conflicts of interest prevented natural regeneration from taking place over extensive areas. This situation was alleviated only when questions of land tenure were eventually clarified. But the truly decisive factor in the recovery of Swiss forests was the importation of coal as a source of energy, starting around 1860, together with subsequent social and economic development. Today, the energy system is still crucial to forest utilisation and the health of Switzerland's forests.

Everything was well prepared. The previous autumn, just before the first snowfall, district forester Karl Kasthofer rode once again to Meiringen, in the area of the Bernese Oberland known as the Haslital, to lay his plans before the communal authorities. He had proposed a tree-planting project on a local mountainside, the Hasliberg, on a slope obliquely facing the Reichenbach Valley with its famous waterfalls. Now, on a glorious day in March which signalled that spring had finally arrived, the warm *föhn* wind was making sparkling ripples on Lake Brienz and rapidly melting the snow on the surrounding mountain slopes. With any luck, thought Kasthofer, the trees could be in the ground before the *föhn* disappeared, which would allow them to benefit from the ensuing rains.

Thousands of larch saplings cultivated in Kasthofer's nursery on a hill known as *der Kleine Rugen* lay ready, bundled together and wrapped in wet flour sacks. As labourers loaded the young trees onto a waiting barge moored at the bank of the Aare River, the forester repeatedly cautioned them to keep the sacks damp so that the roots would not dry out, and to plant the saplings carefully and surround them with prickly twigs of wild rose to protect them from damage by browsing livestock.

Overpopulation or Not Enough to Eat?

Karl Kasthofer had been appointed just a few years previously – in 1806 to be exact – as the first district forester in the Bernese Oberland. He was one of the first foresters in the Alps with academic training, having studied in Germany at the universities of Heidelberg and Göttingen, and also at a forestry school in the Harz Mountains. His education was not confined to the study of trees and the principles of forestry, however. His thinking was also influenced by Adam Smith's concept of the 'invisible hand', with its vision of universal freedom and prosperity, and by the ideas of the economist Thomas Malthus. Like Malthus, Kasthofer believed that the struggle

to increase food production in order to meet the needs of a growing population would be a race between the hare and the tortoise. This led him to make what efforts he could in the early years of the nineteenth century to endow the tortoise with faster legs – to improve the yields obtained from forest, field and meadow.[1]

Subsistence farming was the basis of the economy in the Bernese Oberland of Kasthofer's day. Cheese and other dairy products were the main dietary staples, along with potatoes and various cereal crops, which were grown in garden-like fashion on the floors of valleys.[2] The poor lived mainly on goat's milk and potatoes. Meat was a luxury, even in the homes of the well-to-do. Although animal husbandry was combined with crop cultivation to help reduce the risks inherent in agriculture, it was not always possible to ward off hunger, especially in cases where little remained after an inheritance had been shared, debt had accumulated, or families had to make do without land of their own. Commerce was still conducted on a small scale, with trade restricted to a limited number of commodities. Cheese and cows were exported. Imports included iron, salt used to conserve cheese and – as noted with disapproval in parish records – wine, fashionable clothes and coffee, which had been part of the daily diet in the homes of the well-to-do since the 1760s.[3]

There were no external inputs of energy or fertiliser into this system, which was maintained entirely by the sun. Energy was produced biologically, with plants acting as solar collectors. Although the supply of this traditional solar energy was limited, it nevertheless came from a sustainable, renewable source.[4] Agricultural production was also subject to limitations. Constraints were imposed not so much by the lack of land as by the shortage of nutrients to fertilise the soil. Only about one fifth of the animal dung available was actually collected and spread on fields and meadows.[5] As there was so little fertiliser, plants used for fodder grew poorly and were of little nutritional value: cows produced at most two to three litres of milk per day. Crop yields, too, fell far short of their full potential.

Forests as an Economic and Social Buffer

In this world of limited resources, the forest played a central role. Although vast tracts of primary forest had long since disappeared by Kasthofer's time, remote secondary forests still existed in a state close to nature. The mixture of species in forests near settled areas, however, had often been greatly transformed by

centuries of use. Aside from serving as a source of fuel for the open hearth, which required constant supplies of firewood, these forests also supplied leaves. Sickles were used to lop branches from trees, which were then dried in sheltered areas so the leaves could be preserved for use as cattle fodder in winter. Since not much grain was cultivated, little straw was available as a binding agent for cattle dung. Autumn leaves, therefore, were substituted for straw. In Kasthofer's day, it was impossible to find a beech forest anywhere in the Bernese Oberland whose leaves had not been raked up and gathered to be mixed with dung. The compost created from this mixture was the only fertiliser available to spread on fields and meadows.

Animal husbandry, the most important source of food and income, was exploited to the utmost. The chronic lack of fodder forced farmers to use even the forest as a grazing area. Every morning herds of goats fanned out over the slopes above the villages like a swarm of locusts, working their way into the forest higher up, where they devoured every leaf and needle within reach. As an agent of encroaching degradation, the browsing animal is a far greater threat to the forest than the man with an axe; the damage caused by animals impedes natural processes of regeneration. Traditional felling of trees was always done selectively, according to need, with natural regeneration automatically replacing what humans extracted from the forest. Now, however, seedlings were being uprooted by sheep and trampled by cattle, while the few that survived perished after being nibbled to death by goats.

However, it would have been impossible to ban livestock from the forest at this time, because the forest played an important social role. Forest grazing was a consequence of the existing social structure. Depending on the village, up to a quarter of the families then living in the Oberland possessed no land of their own.[6] The prevailing mythology of democracy contrasted with existing conditions, since freedom and equality had not yet taken

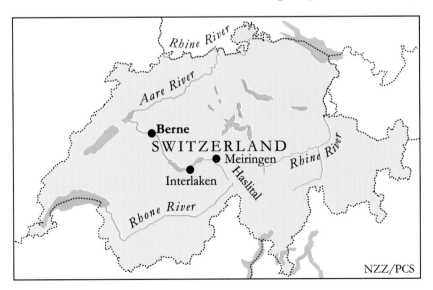

NZZ/PCS

root. The Switzerland of Karl Kasthofer's day was a class society, and the class structure determined access to natural resources. Only long-established families had political rights and private land, as well as the right to use common property: to graze their livestock on meadows in the vicinity of the village or in Alpine pastures during summer, and to harvest fuelwood and timber from the forest. People without land, who were often relatively recent migrants, had only limited access to these valuable resources. The forest was their primary source of livelihood. These people had only petty, unofficial rights, and their presence was merely tolerated. They obtained fuelwood by gathering the branches left behind by those who had the right to use entire trees, and scraped up litter and soil from the forest floor to fertilise the potatoes they grew on tiny patches of leased land.[7]

This landless segment of the population also kept goats, 'the poor man's cow', which browsed in the forest whenever the ground was free of snow. When they required timber for use in construction, or some other resource to which they were not entitled by established rights, people who possessed no land were forced to trespass, helping themselves to whatever they needed to meet their requirements. The more marginal their existence, the more they needed the forest in order to survive.

Karl Kasthofer, Development Expert

Seen from the perspective of the twentieth century, the Bernese Oberland of Kasthofer's day could be roughly compared to what President Harry Truman of the United States described in 1949 as an 'underdeveloped region'.[8] It was from this expression that the term 'developing country' eventually evolved. By today's standards, Kasthofer could indeed be regarded as a kind of early development expert. In his day there was no real distinction between North and South – between developed and developing countries as we know them today. Nevertheless, he identified socio-

economic problems in his own society which he sought to remedy.

In his first years as district forester, Kasthofer devoted himself to technical improvements. In order to conduct his own research, he purchased Alp Abendberg near Interlaken, where he experimented with Kashmir goats from the Himalayas. These animals were valued for their fine, soft wool, and were said to browse modestly, causing little damage to the forest. He also planted Siberian wheat, Spanish clover, and other legumes whose roots contain bacteria that fix nitrogen from the atmosphere, helping to fertilise the soil.

Kasthofer's primary interest, however, was trees. He advised farmers to plant ash and other deciduous species, not only in the forest but also along streams and embankments, as well as in meadows and pastures. He explained that trees, with their extensive root systems and the great surface area of their leaves, were best able to make use of the deeper layers of the soil while also taking advantage of sunlight and air above the ground. Trees would supplement grass by providing leaf fodder. Again and again Kasthofer extolled the virtues of what he called 'meadows in the air'.[9]

His aims were also reflected in the cargo that had been loaded onto the barges bound for Meiringen. Kasthofer especially valued larch, not only because it could be sold as suitable timber for construction, but also because its translucent canopy allowed grass to grow beneath it, while the needles it shed every autumn made excellent fertiliser. He cultivated great numbers of larch trees in his nursery on *der Kleine Rugen*, which he distributed to both communes and private landowners free of charge.[10]

A Smouldering Feud over Land Ownership

A week after the larch saplings were dispatched to Meiringen, Kasthofer happened to be crossing the customs bridge when he saw the barge and its crew moored alongside the quay. Wondering what had been brought back on the

Autumn 1996 on the Kleine Rugen, a hill south of Interlaken, where Karl Kasthofer conducted silvicultural experiments. Kasthofer probably planted some of these yellowing larches himself.

Xaver Siegen, who lives in the Lötschental, is one of the few Swiss farmers who still cut leaf fodder for their cows. For centuries, ash leaves were indispensable as livestock fodder throughout the Alps.

Women in the Canton of Tessin carrying fuelwood down to the valley. Although this picture was taken around the turn of the last century, fuelwood remained an important source of energy in Tessin until the 1950s, as it still is today in the countries of the South.

return trip, he continued across the bridge and hurried down the embankment. To his dismay, he discovered that the barge was loaded with its original cargo – the bundles of larch saplings. Still packed in the same sacks, they were now completely dried out, and their shoots were shrivelled and dead.

The contrite crew then recounted what had happened. They had reached their destination, only to be confronted by farmers who had grazing rights on the Hasliberg. The farmers wanted nothing to do with development aid from a forester who represented the state. They were utterly convinced that once trees were planted on their pastureland, the Canton of Bern would one day claim the right to harvest timber there. While the crew tried to reason with the indignant yeomen, the flour sacks and the sapling roots dried out. The young trees were finally shipped back to Interlaken 'as a protest to make it clear to the district forester that state intrusion of this sort would not be tolerated', as Kasthofer later wrote in describing this memorable incident.[11] Only after retreating to the archives for a careful search of ancient documents did the bewildered forester find an explanation for this singular event. He discovered that the land at Oberhasli had been

the property of the city of Berne since the fourteenth century. As the landlord, the city was entitled to use of the forest. At first, however, rather than exercising its sovereignty, the city granted local farmers extensive rights to graze their animals and harvest timber. The farmers subsequently organised themselves into user groups, which drew up their own regulations and jointly established procedures for using forest resources. After some decades had passed, they had every reason to assume that they alone were entitled to these rights.

However, when iron ore was discovered on the same land in the fifteenth century, the city of Berne granted mining concessions to outsiders, allowing them to cut wood and burn it to obtain charcoal. Although all contracts took care to ensure that the rights of the local inhabitants were respected, the smelting of iron ore required such enormous amounts of fuelwood that infringements became the order of the day. It was not long before conflicts broke out between the local population and the miners.

The mines were abandoned only shortly after Kasthofer took office. Berne, then the most powerful city-state north of the Alps, had for centuries accepted half a tonne of cannon balls as a leasehold rent. And the city had also tried for centuries to ensure that enough timber was available for smelting iron ore. Yet local farmers continued all the while to insist on what they perceived as their rights. They took steps to protect their interests by denying the miners as much timber as they possibly could. They let their livestock graze on cut-over surfaces, and later cleared the land for cultivation by cutting through the bark of the remaining trees, letting them dry out, and then burning them.

Extensive tracts of forestland were degraded as a result of this long-running dispute, and some forests disappeared completely. Even today trees still do not grow in many places where avalanches and rock-falls subsequently cut a swath through the forest. In the final analysis, the barge-load of dried-out larches was an expression of this centuries-old conflict, exemplifying the historic resistance of the people of the Haslital to what they perceived as the power of a haughty overlord. It was in this same spirit of resistance that they refused the aid offered by district forester Kasthofer, who was, after all, a representative of the state.

Berne as a 'Black Hole'

Like all other towns at the time, Berne acted as a 'black hole', devouring enormous amounts of energy and raw materials from its surroundings. As early as the fourteenth century its citizens tried to conserve their forests by means of strict regulations. Later, it was stipulated exactly who could use wood for cooking and heating, and in what amounts. Yet despite warnings against wanton consumption and waste of a resource 'for which we are responsible to our children and children's children',[12] by about 1800 the citizens of Berne, who numbered some 12,000 at the time, were consuming around 50,000 cubic metres of wood per year.[13]

In a quest to satisfy its demand for energy, the city of Berne extended its search for wood to the Bernese Oberland. Rafting timber down the Aare River was not only an easy way to ensure supplies of wood but an inexpensive

one as well, as the city could reclaim its sovereignty anywhere in the Oberland. The well-to-do citizens of Berne were thus putting as much pressure on forest resources as the landless rural population.

Kasthofer repeatedly condemned official imports of timber by the city as a strategy to 'avert the so-called shortage of wood' in order to keep prices low.[14] In his opinion, this artificial reduction in the price of a resource that was indispensable for producing energy not only hampered energy-saving innovations which could 'protect individual rooms and entire houses from the cold',[15] but also undermined the potential for conserving wood through the use of improved stoves and ovens.

Interventions by the powerful city of Berne provoked resistance everywhere in the Bernese Oberland. As early as the eighteenth century, the people of Interlaken sent a note of protest to Berne complaining about clear-cutting on *der Grosse Rugen*. Shortly before the revolution of 1798, a commune in which Berne had been asserting its sovereignty won a lawsuit against the city. This subsequently triggered an avalanche of similar court cases.

A mountain forest in the Lötschental (right), and timber from a clear-cut area around the turn of the last century in the Steinbachwald near the city of Chur (above). Extensive woodlands existed in the Alps, but there was no local demand for their timber. On the other hand, urban demand for energy and raw materials caused a steady drain on Alpine forest resources. With reference to the clear-cutting done in the Oberland by the city of Berne, Karl Kasthofer noted that the true value of timber and the market price for wood were two very different things. The modest prices paid by the city for timber fell far short of reflecting the real value of the forest and its protective functions, which benefited local populations as well as people living downstream. Kastfhofer was convinced that the more communes and private interests earned from selling timber, the better care they would take of their forests, and the more likely it was that raw exploitation would be replaced by sustainable forestry.

of the Canton of Berne to the valley floors of the Oberland. Stalls were expanded to include troughs for collection of liquid manure, making it possible to retain the urine which contained half of all the nitrogen excreted by animals and which had previously seeped unused into the ground.[23] Thanks to more intense fertilisation and the planting of clover-like legumes to be used as fodder, both the quality and the quantity of cattle feed were enhanced. Milk production soon doubled, and there was a boom in cheese exports.[24] In many places commons which had long served as community grazing land were divided up into private plots and converted to potato fields, which became highly productive with sufficient inputs of fertiliser.

The winds of change were also blowing across the political landscape. The liberals who triumphed in the elections of 1831 provided the Canton of Berne with a new constitution in the same year that did away with hereditary privilege, guaranteeing equal rights to all citizens, while also removing all restrictions on agriculture, commerce and trade.[25] The concept of private property, understood as complete individual control over a particular possession, was the guiding principle on which these changes were based. Traditional forms of communal ownership, by contrast, now appeared as the main obstacle to a free market economy and economic growth.

Reform Extends to Forestry

Karl Kasthofer consistently emphasised that liberal reforms also had to be extended to the realm of forestry. He urged that forests in which different owners had different rights and interests should be divided up in such a way that each individual could use or improve his own parcel of land in accordance with his own wishes, 'unhindered by lazy, envious or ignorant fellow owners.'[26] Forests which were not heavily used could still be reserved for communal purposes. Kasthofer did not intend to completely deregulate forestry, however.[27]

Previous page: Careful timber
cutting, which involves precise
calculations to within
centimetres, plays an important
role in protecting natural
regeneration. In Switzerland,
large-scale clear-cutting, with
subsequent planting of
monocultures that result in
chessboard forests, was
abandoned at the end of the
last century in favour of single-
stem selective felling or felling
in small gaps that facilitates
natural regeneration (above).

His goal was to establish a legal framework providing specific guidelines, above all for the use of mountain forests. He knew that the forests would have to be used sustainably in order to preserve their protective function. He defined sustainable use – a key concept in forestry – to mean that timber should not be felled at a rate which exceeded the rate of natural growth.[28] He envisioned that the implementation of such regulations would be overseen by a forestry service, whose personnel could also offer technical advice to those who owned and tried to manage forestland. The experts to staff this service would be trained in a special forestry school. The entire operation would be financed by a tax on timber exported by the Canton of Berne.

In 1836 Karl Kasthofer was elected to serve as a minister in the cantonal government. Three years later, his administration secured the passage of a law providing for the separation of forests and pastures.[29] Although it often took decades before grazing rights on forestland were rescinded, trees were eventually able to regenerate wherever this did happen. A subsequent law clarified rights to timber use, allowing forests to be specifically divided between the state and groups who possessed rights of use, in order to put an end once and for all to the age-old disputes between the urban and rural populations of the Canton of Berne. This change in the regulations initially had mixed results, however. Privileged members of rural society were still able to make their interests prevail and to block progress on some of the legal measures advocated by Kasthofer, such as a competent forest service staffed by qualified experts.

The provision that forestland could further be divided up among individual beneficiaries caused additional problems. Forestland privatised on this basis was frequently clear-cut, with the timber sold for cash, either to pay off debts on a farmstead or to take advantage of the new current of economic liberalism before the political climate changed once again.[30] Kasthofer's successors eventually came to the conclusion that communal ownership was better for the forest than private ownership, not only because good forestry requires planning and action over generations, but also because a minimum area must be involved if the forest is to be managed rationally.

Even more far-reaching in terms of its ultimate impact on the volume and quality of forest stands was the fact that not every family obtained rights of use in the forest, despite the guarantee of equality to every citizen in the new cantonal constitution. In practice, members of the rural upper class succeeded in exercising the privileges to which they were entitled by birth. In an ominous twist of fate, the petty customary rights which had long been tolerated out of 'good-heartedness' were now abolished.[31] This occurred despite Kasthofer's continual warnings that the old order must not simply be replaced by 'a new aristocracy of large landowners and people of great wealth' while the under-privileged, who had no legally established rights, were excluded from the forest, thereby destroying traditional social niches.[32]

In 1835 an organisation of landless citizens reported that both established and newly privileged social groups were claiming extravagant amounts of timber for personal use, and enriching themselves by selling it, causing long-term ruin to the forests.[33] The fact that timber had now gained actual monetary value in 1830 and could be sold was a consequence of the general economic development then taking place throughout Europe; timber was a necessary commodity in the expanding economy of the day. At the same time, the denial of social justice for all made thieves of those who had been excluded from the new economic order. Pillaging of the forest now took place on a massive scale, increasing in direct proportion to the rise in the price of timber.[34]

The Alps of Yesterday Foreshadow the Tropics of Today

Crews working for timber merchants now began to appear in the Oberland, 'advancing in an unbroken line with their merciless axes.'[35] Shipbuilding and harbour construction in

India

Resolving Conflicts to Protect Siva's Locks

In the nineteenth century British colonial administrators in India took control of vast areas of forestland, which they subsequently exploited through the Imperial Forest Service. A good part of this forestland had originally been managed communally in accordance with local rules and regulations. With the coming of the British Raj (colonial rule), conflicts broke out between rural populations and the Forest Service. Village systems of resource use broke down, and forest degradation accelerated rapidly. The Chipko Movement, founded in the 1970s with the aim of conserving forests in the Himalayas, is one recent response to these developments. Before the Himalayas can become green again, however, it will be necessary to resolve long-running conflicts. Here, just as in other areas of the world, conservation and regeneration of forests are primarily a social problem and only secondarily a biological problem. No one has demonstrated this more convincingly than Visheswar Dutt Saklani, the man who planted 30,000 trees.

According to Hindu legend, the sacred River Ganges originated not on earth but in heaven, for it was said to emanate from Vishnu's toe. Legend also has it that when the 60,001 ill-bred sons of King Sagara disturbed the sage Kapila while he was meditating, he reduced them to ashes with one scorching glance. Saint Bhagiratha then prayed for the Ganges to be brought down to earth so its waters could cleanse the ashes. The river goddess Ganga, furious at being displaced from heaven, stormed through the gorges of the Himalayas and onto the plain, where she unleashed a torrent of floods and destruction. Anxious to rescue the earth, Siva, the most benevolent of the gods, caught the turbulent river on his brow and stilled Ganga's fury in his matted locks.

Just as he does every evening, Visheswar Dutt Saklani sat monotonously reciting from the Puranas, the Hindu scriptures which tell of the creation, destruction and rebirth of the universe, and which are the source of the legend explaining how the Ganges came down to earth.[1] We were sitting on a *charpoy*: a bedstead woven from straw with four posts. The flame of a kerosene lamp intensified the light of dusk that was streaming through the one small window. In the kitchen, Saklani's wife and daughter were finishing what remained of our supper of rice and *dal*: a tangy curry made from lentils. A woman balancing a full pitcher of water on her head passed by outside. When Saklani paused in his chanting, I could hear the soft chewing sounds made by the water buffalo that was tethered beneath the window.

Visheswar Dutt Saklani is a farmer. He lives in the Song Valley in a village called Saklana, nestled in the foothills which rise from the floodplains of the Ganges and Indus rivers to form a broad band in the foreground beneath the great peaks of the Himalayas. The catchment area of the Song, which merges with the Ganges further downstream, is part of Garhwal and lies between Kumaon to the east and the state of Himachal Pradesh to the west. Garhwal and Kumaon together comprise the highland areas of the state of Uttar Pradesh. I first heard of Visheswar Dutt Saklani in 1984, when Sunderlal Bahuguna told me of 'the man who planted 30,000 trees'. Bahuguna, in Europe at the time, was one of the leaders of the grass-roots Chipko Movement, which was founded in the 1970s to conserve Himalayan forests in India. The next year I had a chance to spend five months journeying through the Hindu Kush and the Himalayas, travelling from Pakistan through India to Nepal. The village of Saklana was my first destination after I reached the foothills of the Indian Himalayas. It was not difficult to find Visheswar Dutt Saklani; he was well known here for having raised literally tens of thousands of trees, which had since become an entire oak forest. He was the man who cared for Siva's locks and watched over their regeneration. In the Himalayan foothills of India, Siva's bountiful locks of hair are, of course, a metaphor for the forest.

The story of Saklani's forest began with a tragic event in January 1947, the day on which

Previous page: View to the north of Shimla, the main city in the state of Himachal Pradesh. The broad band of hills lies in the foreground of the snow-covered Himalayan peaks. 'Siva's locks', the forests which diminish the force of runoff during the monsoon season, have now largely disappeared.

Visheswar Dutt Saklani, 'the man who planted 30,000 trees'. Part of his forest can be seen in the background.

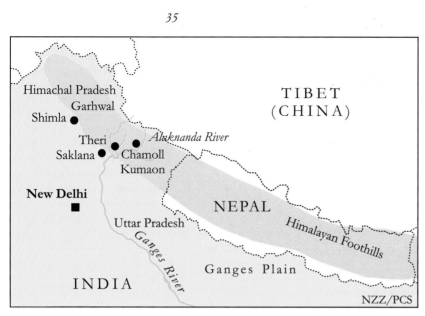

day. Then it is time to nurse the baby, tidy up, mop the mud floor, and perhaps be on call to dress a child's wounded foot with blood-staunching herbs. During the dry season, when up to 80 per cent of the livestock feed is supplied by the evergreen white oak, the afternoons are also taken up with the search for leaf fodder.[2] Long after dusk, completely exhausted, the women collapse on their sleeping mats before the kitchen fire.

The daily routine of the men is quite different – provided that they are living at home and have not migrated to the plains to seek jobs. They do periodic heavy labour, such as clearing land or improving terraces on cultivated areas when necessary. In addition, they have religious duties and they also do the ploughing, since ploughing is a task forbidden to Hindu women. Nevertheless, there is plenty of time to discuss politics outside the tea stall or the liquor booth. It would be difficult, however, to find another man who spends his time as Visheswar Dutt Saklani does, campaigning to restore the forest – the very foundation of the land-use system here.

Receding Trees and Declining Fertility

The forest in the Himalayas plays the same role today that it did in the Alps when life there was still dependent on traditional solar energy. Two harvests a year – rice and millet in the monsoon season and wheat in winter – take a heavy toll on nutrients in the soil. To make up for the shortage of nutrients it is necessary to collect organic matter in the form of leaf fodder and leaf litter over extensive areas of the forest, which may be as large as 30 times the size of a typical cultivated field.[3] Domestic animals also play an important role in this process, as they transform fresh leaves into compost. Milk production, however, is often of secondary importance: yields average two to three litres per day – the equivalent of what Alpine cows produced in Karl Kasthofer's day.

Although every child knows that trees are the mother of fruitful fields, Siva's locks are now found only on hilltops and in inaccessible

for Indian independence. In his grief, he decided to establish a forest in his brother's memory. Each year on 11 January, friends and relations gather with Saklani to plant more trees, which have since grown to constitute a forest of oak larger than 20 football fields.

The Daily Struggle to Secure a Livelihood

I was awakened before daybreak by the clattering of dishes in the kitchen. Smoke from a freshly kindled fire and the cheerful voices of Saklani's wife and sister-in-law drifted through the cracks in the mud wall. I marvel at these women, who have just begun another hard day's work. Even in this relatively prosperous household their tasks are strenuous. Daily toil of this sort frequently drives many other women beyond the limits of their endurance.

The workday starts early. First the women must fetch water and grind wheat for making bread. After they see to the needs of the men and children and milk the buffalo, they set out for the forest. Often accompanied by neighbours, they are equipped with sickles and carrying-straps to cut fuelwood and gather grass and leaf fodder for the animals. Bearing bundles that I could barely lift, let alone carry for hours, they trudge home before noon to prepare the midday meal – if they happen to belong to a family that can afford three meals a now found only on hilltops and in inaccessible places in the Song Valley. This is the case practically everywhere in the Himalayan foothills, and in most other parts of the country as well. Consequently, women have to make a greater effort every year to collect leaves, putting themselves increasingly at risk when lopping off branches and returning home with the fodder. Constraints on their time invariably force them to exploit the nearest trees, often before the ideal recovery period of two to three years has elapsed.[4] The trees die more rapidly as a result, and the margins of the forest become frayed from this nibbling effect and steadily recede.[5]

If the distance between the village and the forest becomes too great, or if there are no more trees, women can no longer bring home enough organic matter to keep the nutrient supply in balance. It then becomes necessary to burn dried dung instead of fuelwood, which further exacerbates the fertiliser deficit. The immediate consequences are poorer harvests and even lower yields of buffalo milk. In order to compensate for food shortages, women are sometimes forced to sell the gold jewellery which they had originally intended to keep as a dowry for their daughters. Another strategy for survival is to keep greater numbers of goats, which are more adept than other animals at finding enough food to sustain themselves in a degraded environment. Goats are steadily increasing in number in Saklana and its surroundings, as they are in most Himalayan villages. Nation-wide, the goat population doubled between 1950 and 1980.[6] However, as goats prefer young saplings and other woody vegetation, they hinder natural forest regeneration, further intensifying processes of degradation.

The Empire Extends its Hegemony to the Foothills

All things considered, present-day conditions in the Himalayas appear hauntingly reminiscent of nineteenth-century conditions in the Alps.

However, there is a fundamental difference in historical development between the Alps and the Himalayas. While the British came to the Alps as tourists, they came to the Himalayas first as traders, and later as rulers who established the British Raj. Almost from the outset the British sought to clear the land and break new ground for the cultivation of export crops. For example, the area around Gorakhpur, at the base of the Himalayan foothills on the Ganges Plain, was densely covered with sal trees until the early part of the nineteenth century.[7] The bamboo-covered banks of the river were swollen by Ganga's fury in the monsoon season. Swamps filled with mosquitoes became breeding grounds for malaria, which spread swiftly and deterred settlement in the area for a long time. Owing to the great desire for land, however, British 'sugar barons' cleared tens of thousands of hectares of forestland for cultivation by 1830.[8]

The hills were spared a little longer. In 1838 a British colonial official reported that nowhere else in the world did farmers have such good clothes or such well-built houses as in Garhwal and Kumaon. As late as 1850 hillfarmers still did not bother to gather the wild fruits and vegetables in the nearby forest, for their own harvests were so plentiful that they could afford to export grain to Tibet and the Ganges Plain.[9] In 1855 a British promoter of the iron industry described the forests of Garhwal and Kumaon as 'boundless and inexhaustible' and reported that the forests at every mining site 'can supply sufficient charcoal for the largest English furnace for 100 years to come'.[10]

Yet the hills, too, gradually succumbed to the influence of colonialism. Hill stations such as Musoorie or Shimla, now part of the state of Himachal Pradesh, were established not far from Saklana in the foothills at the base of the Himalayas. In 1864, Shimla became the summer capital for British colonial officials. Located at an altitude of more than 2100 metres, it was a bit cooler in the hot season prior to the monsoon.

Forest destruction followed hard on the heels of British colonialists in the hills, as it did

Saklani's 40-year-old wife (wearing a red scarf) and her sister.

wherever else they went. The hill stations rapidly became 'black holes', just as the city of Berne had once been. Wood was needed to fire limestone, and enormous quantities of timber were required for the construction of government offices and official residences, which were architecturally similar to the hotels being built in Interlaken in the same period. Newly cultivated fields nearby were used to grow products for side dishes to accompany the salmon imported from Scotland and the Mediterranean sardines that were served in these stylish dwelling-places. At the same time, timber was being steadily harvested from the Himalayan forests to meet the requirements of economic development on the plains, where timber stocks were gradually being depleted. In 1844 an English contractor named Wilson obtained a concession from the Raj (feudal lord) of Tehri-Garhwal, allowing him to harvest Himalayan cedars, which grew at altitudes above 1800 metres and had to be rafted for months down the Ganges to reach the plains.[11] Wilson's contract permitted him to fell as many trees as he wanted at a fee of 400 rupees per year for 20 years; yet within only one decade, he had already ravished the most magnificent cedar stands.[12]

Railways Transform the World of Commerce

In 1853 the British began constructing a railway network to connect main harbours and major cities with the fertile hinterlands. Vast areas which had previously been part of a local, or at most a regional, economic system were directly linked to the international commodities market. Increasingly larger areas of the country were now drawn into the vortex of global commerce conducted by the British Empire.

Cotton from the hinterland of Bombay fed the looms of Manchester, a major centre of the textile industry in England. Indigo from the freshly cleared Ganges Plain was used to dye cloth exported to North America as denim, which was subsequently fashioned into durable bluejeans worn by cowboys and gold prospectors. Wheat from the Punjab sustained office clerks in London, the administrative centre of the Empire, where construction of the London Underground was begun in 1863 in order to ease crowding caused by the throng of commuters during rush hours. Aside from facilitating exports, India's railways also opened up an enormous market for industrial products imported from Britain, such as machine-woven cottons, which rapidly displaced domestically produced goods and elaborate handmade Indian artefacts.

With approximately 1800 sleepers needed for every mile of track, the railway network consumed incredible quantities of timber. Some 66 million sleepers were required for the 37,000 miles (60,000 kilometres) laid by 1920, which comprised only the first generation of railway construction.[13]

The Calcutta–Varanasi–Allahabad line running parallel to the Ganges was completed by 1859. The next step was to link the fertile plains of Uttar Pradesh and the Punjab to the network. Construction of this link was a priority, for this area had been the site of the recent Sepoy Uprising, the final effort of the rajahs of northern India to shake off colonial rule. If troops could be rapidly transported by rail, it would be possible to quell any such uprisings in the future.[14] But sal trees, which had once existed in great abundance at the base of the Himalayan foothills and which were the best-suited trees in the region for making sleepers, had long since been cleared away by the sugar barons.

The railway builders therefore turned their attention to Himalayan cedar, the last species still growing in large stands which was suitable to the needs of empire. In the early 1860s, however, the British army surgeon and botanist Hugh Cleghorn conducted a survey which showed that most cedar stands were on property that belonged to Indian rajahs, who had often granted concessions to people such as Wilson at give-away prices. Signs of a threatening shortage of wood soon led to the establishment of the Forest Department in 1864. A year later, Dietrich Brandis, a German who had worked many years for the British in the teak forests of Burma, was appointed as the first inspector general of forests in India. In the following decades, the Imperial Forest Service focused its attention largely on the Himalayas, from whose forests 1.3 million cedar railway sleepers had already been extracted by 1878.[15]

Rights of Use: the Roots of a Still Unresolved Conflict

In precolonial times the local rajahs exercised sovereignty over the Himalayan forests, just as the city of Berne had exercised its sovereignty in Oberhasli in the Bernese Oberland. The rajahs held their forestland in reserve for their courtiers or used it to remunerate soldiers.[16] But aside from their value in sustaining elephants, which were important in wartime, forest products aroused real interest only when wood later became a valuable commodity in the British market economy.

Farmers had long been allowed to use forest products; only if they had enough leaf fodder for their cattle and enough compost to fertilise their fields could they pay the taxes which provided the upkeep of the rajahs' opulent courts. For similar reasons, colonial authorities had long recognised communal rights of use in local forests, until the shortage of wood for sleepers made even remote forest stands important to the aims of the Empire.[17] Farmers did not have open access to forest resources, however. On the contrary, forests in the vicinity of villages were often managed as common property according to specific rules. They were frequently surrounded by stone walls to protect them from cattle, and the village council or the village elders stipulated the times and the conditions under which common rights of use could be exercised.[18] Clear rules governing the use of woodlands far from villages were also likely to be established in the course of time. Even remote forests, which would not be perceived by outsiders as having any connection with the village economy, constituted special sites that were reserved as the dwelling-places of gods and spirits whom local people did not dare to disturb.

Deeply rooted conflicts over resource use and serious conflicts of interest between local populations and the Forest Service soon became apparent in the foothills of the Himalayas, just as they once had in the Alps. It must be emphasised that Cleghorn had

Traditional fertiliser for agricultural fields in the Himalayas still consists of animal dung mixed with leaf litter from the forest. Artificial fertiliser is rarely used.

Sacred trees, curative plants. Forest degradation cannot be attributed to negative or indifferent attitudes among rural people. Hindus believe that many trees are the dwelling places of gods and benevolent spirits. The Hindu god Vishnu was born under the banyan tree (above). It is forbidden to touch this tree with iron, and cutting its branches is said to bring a fatal curse upon one's family.

proposed as early as 1861 that both the right to harvest timber and the obligation to regenerate the forest should be handed over to local people, since they had the greatest interest in maintaining the forests and managing them to obtain sustainable yields.[19] Brandis, too, had entertained notions of allowing local communities to retain control over forest resources. But the Revenue Department, which was responsible for collecting taxes, opposed the legalisation of traditional village-level forest management practices, fearing both loss of revenue and loss of influence.[20]

Most of the staff of the Imperial Forest Service were officers seconded from the police force or the army, whose attitude towards villagers was much like the attitude of a Victorian husband towards his wife. In paternalistic fashion, these officials contended that local people were not capable of managing the forests, and that they needed protection from the consequences of their own negligence, which could easily cause destruction of the forests as well as erosion problems.[21] Here, again, the vocabulary used by colonial foresters betrayed their true aims. Officials in the Imperial Forest Service used the expression 'minor forest products' – the word 'minor' hinting at

inferiority – in the same way that it had been used by their counterparts in Europe. This contrasted with the 'major' forest product: the timber that was considered crucial not only to 'the advance of civilisation' but also to vital 'national interests'.[22]

The arrogance of power became transparent at a Forest Service conference in 1875, where it was openly maintained that the 'victor' is entitled to enjoy the 'rights of conquest'.[23] This statement was a clear admission of the rationale behind the setting aside of reserved forests, in accordance with provisions contained in the Forest Act of 1878. Reserved forests were foreseen wherever timber could be produced profitably or wherever the forest had a protective function. A reserved forest became the property of the colonial government as soon as existing rights, such as the right to obtain leaf fodder or to graze goats, were rescinded. News of such decisions was then gazetted on public notice boards to inform the local population. Reserved forests frequently constituted half of the total area of a village.[24] But local farming populations had never been willing to see their traditional rights curtailed, and they vigorously opposed expropriations of land. From this time forward, as a forestry official remarked in 1893, the practice of forestry became an ongoing struggle with village-dwellers.[25]

Fire Becomes a Sign of Resistance

The relationship between the Forest Service and the population in Kumaon reached a new low point at the beginning of the twentieth century. Owing to World War I, there was a sudden interest in a species of pine known as *chir* – the most important source of resin and turpentine in the entire British Empire.[26] In 1920, the number of pine trees tapped for resin in Kumaon alone far exceeded the two million mark.[27] The Forest Service rapidly tried to exert its control over this resource by putting these trees in newly established reserved forests, further eroding local rights.

Instructions for the use of medicinal herbs were recorded 3000 years ago in the Ayur Veda, known as the 'holy book of life'. Medicinal applications described in this ancient text cover over a thousand plants, many of which grow in forests.

In 1920 Mohandas Gandhi, who was to lead India to independence in 1947 and later become known to the world as Mahatma ('great soul'), began his first nation-wide campaign of civil disobedience to protest against unjust laws. Gandhi characterised the newly established forest reserves as a symbol of oppression. In the following year, the local population set fire to forests of *chir* just before the monsoon, as they had always done, so that the ensuing rains would promote the growth of hardy fodder in soil fertilised by ashes. But this time the fires raged more widely and intensely than before, consuming hundreds of thousands of pines. This initial regional protest by people in the Himalayan foothills forced the government to abandon the newly established reserved forests.[28]

The People versus the Foresters

The population of India grew steadily from 1920 onwards, especially in the lowlands. Timber was increasingly rafted from the hills to the lowlands, where it was needed for energy as well as for construction. Often it was auctioned off before being felled, as the Forest Service could only do a minimal amount of the felling itself. Prosperous contractors from the higher castes recruited outsiders who were more willing to work in the forests for lower wages than the indigenous population.[29] After trees had been cut under these conditions, the forest floor, littered with woody debris and branches, resembled a battlefield.

While forestry officials closed their eyes to slipshod felling and the inclination of contractors to fell timber even where it was not marked, they exercised strict police powers in dealing with local people. They destroyed the sickles which women used to cut branches, and meted out severe punishment even for minor offences. It was not surprising, then, that the Forest Service, a tightly organised hierarchy where even the lowest-ranking wardens wore uniforms, was seen by the population as an arrogant and repressive bureaucracy. Even the

integration of increasing numbers of Indian officers into the service after 1920 represented little more than a replacement of the British class system with Indian caste-consciousness.

Repression of the local population did absolutely nothing to preserve the forests, however; on the contrary, it triggered a chain of tragic events that has continued to the present day. Disruption of the delicate balance of power in villages, and the undermining of local customs, were disastrous side-effects of the extension of state jurisdiction. The needs of village-dwellers might have been met despite the reduced amount of forestland available if appropriate new rules had been drawn up to regulate the use of forest resources. But the Forest Service largely refrained from involvement in this sticky task. Consequently, in the place of traditional rules and restrictions, a profound uncertainty about rights arose. Influential villagers quickly moved to fill this vacuum. They obtained fodder from trees traditionally reserved for others. And, responding to the opportunities offered by new markets, they exploited timber to which they would not have had normal access.

Exploitation now replaced more or less sustainable management of forest resources. A tree which has been assigned to the use of a

The slopes of the Himalayas still come under heavy pressure from grazing. Both domestic animals and nomadic herds (left), tended by pastoralists such as Gaddhi shepherds (above), are a threat to regeneration of trees. The valleys through which large herds of Kashmir goats and sheep are driven to summer pastures in the Himalayan highlands are often severely deforested. These animals traditionally spend the winter on fertile fields at the foot of the Himalayas, where shepherds help with the harvesting of crops such as sugar cane. The animals graze on crop residues and their dung replaces valuable nutrients in the soil. Increasing mechanisation and greater use of artificial fertilisers are making this long-established practice superfluous, however, and these winter grazing sites are disappearing. Many large herds are now being dissolved, with the result that trees will be more likely to flourish.

particular family by tradition will be seen as a living resource, and it will be allowed to coppice. But if trees suddenly belong to everyone, there is no longer any guarantee that caring for them will bring benefits, since a tree that has been carefully tended by one person may well be cut down for firewood by someone else later the same day. Nor is there any certainty that a tree planted today can be used ten years hence, either by the person who planted it or by his or her successors.

The estrangement of local populations from their traditional resources also had disastrous effects on reserved forests. The Indian Forest Service made a steady effort to manage reserved forests according to the principles of scientific forestry. But ivory-tower approaches to forestry which exclude local communities from participation were doomed to failure in India, just as they had been earlier in Europe. Local practices, such as using sickles and setting fires that will later promote the growth of animal fodder, cannot be controlled or prevented, either by law or by forestry officials. Nor can herdsmen be stopped from dismantling the fences and walls erected by the Forest Service to keep goats away from cut-over areas. The problem is not timber use *per se*, for natural regeneration is a strong enough force to ensure that forests endure, even in the Himalayas. Other factors such as population growth, the expansion of cropland and grazing areas, and village forest management practices that are not always optimal have undoubtedly contributed to deforestation. But even this combination of factors is not enough to explain the extensive decline of Himalayan forests. The tragedy that has afflicted these commons stems primarily from the dissolution of traditional rights and social structures.[30] Confirmation of this can be seen in regions where access is difficult and where traditional forms of local organisation have been maintained; here significant tracts of forest have often survived.[31]

Independence and the Conflict with China

At the time India won its independence in 1947, its soils were degraded, its economy crippled, its system of property ownership was unbalanced, and its population was growing rapidly. While the railway in Europe functioned mainly as a vehicle of supply, in India it increasingly drained the country's resources. In Europe the railway was an instrument of overall socio-economic improvement which narrowed the gap between the city and the countryside and had a beneficial impact on forests in the long run. In colonial India, however, it had the effect of driving the rural and urban worlds even further apart.

Urban areas had a growing need for railway sleepers and cellulose, while the demand for leaves and other non-timber forest products remained unchanged in rural regions. At the same time, both rural and urban populations burned wood to produce energy. The forests of the newly independent nation had no time to recover. As the rural and urban worlds both sought to satisfy their needs, age-old conflicts continued in the forests of modern India, with most foresters representing urban interests, as they had previously done. On the day before his life came to a violent end in January 1948, Mahatma Gandhi bade his followers to return to the villages. Here, as devotees of *sarvodaya* ('for the general well-being'),[32] they would help village-dwellers to achieve *ramraj*, or the Kingdom of God, as Gandhi called his vision of an India where justice ruled. As he envisioned it, democratic village-republics would one day be largely self-sufficient, and people would no longer have to exploit the land, animals or other human beings. Gandhi was convinced that the earth could provide enough to support a simple life for everyone, provided that people did not aspire to an 'American standard of living.'[33]

Gandhi's plea for a return to village autonomy and a small-scale economy had no chance of acceptance, however, for it was soon

Box 2.1 A divided society

India has been radically transformed since the 1980s. Particularly notable has been the growth of its middle class. Even Hindu culture – traditionally characterised by an emphasis on the superiority of the spiritual and the religious over the material, and capable of being deeply moved by ascetics such as Mahatma Gandhi – is becoming increasingly oriented towards the modern consumer societies found in the developed world. By the mid 1990s, approximately 200 million people in India had achieved a relatively comfortable standard of living. Their India is the land of the Maruti, a middle class car which is slowly taking its place alongside the ubiquitous 'Ambassador'. It is the India that has the know-how to produce atomic weapons and the rockets to fire them, the India of motor scooters, refrigerators and air conditioners. It is also the India of the Green Revolution, which has been respon-sible for making the country self-sufficient in food production, thanks to irrigation, chemical fertilisers and high-yielding crop varieties.

Prosperity in the cities has increased the pressure on forests, as the growing purchasing power of an industrialised India continues to trigger new types of demand. Wood is used for construction, and the demand for modern furniture continues to grow. Consumption of paper is rising rapidly, while marginal populations in the cities still need wood as a source of household energy. Between 1975 and 1985 the price of fuelwood rose twice as fast as the price of food.[49]

The other India – the India of the underprivileged – is a country of 700 million people who live partly in urban slums, but largely in rural areas. Bicycles, torches, kerosene lamps, radios and the occasional television set are among the few products of the industrialised world that can be found in India's 600,000 villages. Yet people at the margins of Indian society are still largely dependent on traditional forest products. As they are hardly able to afford artificial fertiliser for their fields, dried cattle dung must all too often be substituted for fuelwood.

The relationship between urban and rural society in India is similar to that between developed countries and Third World countries: it is characterised by features of colonialism. Prices for rural products such as food, wood and fibres are often insufficient to cover production costs. The terms of trade between city and countryside are thus marked by the same inequity that exists in trade between industrialised and developing countries, particularly where market conditions are distorted by bureaucracy and governmental intervention. The rural population is also at a disadvantage in terms of services such as energy, drinking water and education, which are either openly or indirectly subsidised in the cities.

These social disparities also have many negative impacts on the urban world. Urban demand accelerates degradation of rural resources. Together with the material promise of urban life, this demand is responsible for a rural exodus and the rapid growth of urban slums. Between 1981 and 1991 alone, India's cities absorbed an additional 60 million people, with a corresponding increase in the threat of epidemics.[50] Soils in rural areas, particularly those that are overused, are being continually eroded; water reservoirs are filling up more rapidly with eroded material, and the useful life of both reservoirs and electric power plants is being drastically reduced. This degradation of natural resources will continue until adjustments are made to promote more equitable relations between the worlds of the privileged and the underprivileged.[51]

Chipko activists such as
Sunderlal Bahuguna, explaining
the spiritual and economic
significance of forests to school
children in Shimla, have done
much to draw attention to long-
running conflicts over forest
resources.

Movement was formed when the Forest Service did nothing to halt the activities of contractors who were felling 35 trees per hectare instead of the stipulated two per hectare.[41]

Success at the Local Level Takes Many Forms

As early as the 1970s, the government of Uttar Pradesh began to react to growing popular pressure, which Sunderlal Bahuguna had applied with particular effect in the form of various fasts. Timber felling was temporarily forbidden in certain regions, the contractor system was suspended, and organised felling was delegated to a newly formed governmental forestry corporation. In 1975, the year following the protest in Reni, the *Sangh* began a reforestation campaign. Foresters offered members of the association advice on how to establish a nursery. Close collaboration rapidly became the order of the day, and the *Sangh* was able to bridge the considerable gap that still existed between the population and the Forest Service. The afforestation projects it organises regularly achieve a high rate of successful growth, in contrast to government projects. Today, the *Sangh* operates the largest voluntary afforestation programme in India.

Other successful initiatives rooted in the Chipko Movement are becoming apparent only now. For example, the forest council in Bacheer, a village high above the Alaknanda, was composed entirely of female Chipko activists at the beginning of the 1990s. The women of the village planted fodder-producing forests in the vicinity of their homes and erected a stone wall around them, hiring a woman forest warden to protect them. Thanks to the backing of international non-governmental organisations such as the Ford Foundation, the women of Bacheer now own productive dairy cattle which have been cross-bred with Jersey cows. The cattle are kept in stalls nearby and fed well to ensure high yields of milk.[42] Measures such as these make it possible to better exploit solar energy and optimise the flow of nutrients. Fodder-producing trees, which Karl Kasthofer referred to as 'meadows in the air', help to meet the demand for animal feed and fuelwood. Keeping animals in stalls makes it easier to collect dung and apply it as fertiliser to enhance soil fertility, and the sale of milk also provides women with a separate source of income. If the entire village eventually

Nepal

The Community Is the Better Forester

Nepal became the focus of growing international concern in the 1970s, when it appeared that the Himalayan foothills were being rapidly eroded due to the increasing pressure of population growth. A large-scale, internationally financed reforestation project was subsequently launched in an attempt to halt the progress of degradation. The project achieved good results in the village of Panchamool, although reforestation efforts elsewhere met with less success. Nevertheless, this nation-wide campaign helped to clarify how the fate of trees is decided: it became obvious that the forests could only be preserved by the people who live in the hills. Upland populations, however, will be neither willing nor able to maintain forests unless they are granted clearly defined, incontestable rights of access to forest resources. The arduous task of establishing a system of clear and balanced rights will be the main challenge faced by the Nepalese Forest Service for decades to come.

agricultural land use, which caused rapid runoff and high rates of erosion, as the main factors responsible for flood catastrophes in the delta of the Ganges and the Brahmaputra rivers. The farmers in the mountains of Nepal and their neighbours – a total of some 33 million people – readily became the scapegoats for the flooding and climate change that had taken place on the vast floodplains of these rivers.[6] The theory even went so far as to suggest that destructive forms of land use practised by these upland populations made virtual hostages of hundreds of millions of people on the plains, constituting a permanent threat to their lives and property.

The theory became a source of political tension between India and Bangladesh, as well as between India and Nepal.[7] Nepalese forestry officials and their foreign partners in development projects were soon engaged in heated debate. The Theory of Himalayan Environmental Degradation also became one of the underlying forces which eventually produced the Community Forestry Development Project.

From Policeman to Consultant

Additional findings, which were later incorporated into the project, came from the village of Thokarpa, which is located in the uplands north-east of Kathmandu. It was here that the Nepalese forester Tej Mahat began working as a district forest officer in 1973.

In a file on pending business which had been left behind by his predecessor, Mahat found a letter from the village of Thokarpa. It stated that the village was no longer willing to cooperate with the Forest Service since the service had done nothing to help conserve the forests; on the contrary, it had contributed to forest destruction. Perplexed, Mahat set off for Thokarpa, where the village head explained the reason for the letter. It seemed that the Forest Service had granted a concession to outsiders, allowing them to extract timber in a forest just below the village, along the banks of the

Sunkosi River. The contractors had cut trees and then transported the timber to Kathmandu. This particular forest, however, was of key importance to the village economy as a source of leaf fodder and firewood.

In the course of a long conversation in 1986, Tej Mahat explained to me that any motivation to protect the forest had dwindled to nothing after this incident, as the people of Thokarpa now felt that no one could be certain when the state might once again appropriate the products of local effort for its own purposes. This story was reminiscent of similar episodes in the Alps and in the Himalayan regions of India: it reflected the classic conflict between rural and urban interests, with the Forest Service as the representative of urban interests.

Although the demand for wood in urban areas did not have as great an impact on forests in the mountains of Nepal as it did in the Indian Himalayas, a great deal of timber was nevertheless exported from the Terai to India. The revenues earned from this export trade accounted for almost half of Nepal's gross national product until the 1950s.[8]

Like many others in his profession, Tej Mahat had trained as a 'timber forester' at the former Imperial Forest School in Dehra Dun, India. He recalls that even in post-colonial times, students were indoctrinated with the idea that forestry officials should keep a distance between themselves and local populations. He and his colleagues were taught 'scientific forestry', a discipline which was destined to be practised in an ivory tower atmosphere. Young students were required to wear ties and dinner jackets in the dining-hall, and much emphasis was placed on how forestry officials should behave.

Tej Mahat began his career in the Terai in the 1960s, where rich forests of sal had survived much longer than they did in the Himalayan foothills of India. Here he tried to apply his training in scientific forestry. But wherever he permitted the felling of timber, emigrants from the hills who were seeking a new source of

The Arun winding its way towards the Ganges. A bright green carpet of freshly planted rice spreads over the irrigated terraces, while the rainfed terraces along the path to Panchamool are planted with maize interspersed with fodder trees.

The typical oval-shaped Gurung house has mud walls and a thatched roof. In the prosperous village of Sirubari, most of these dwellings have now been replaced by more representative stone houses, which are easier to maintain.

government of Nepal and the international donor community. Although the project was only one of many undertakings with similar aims, it was by far the largest, with a budget of 25 million American dollars for the first five years; the World Bank alone contributed 18 million American dollars. The aim of the project – rapid reforestation of the denuded hills – would be achieved by a strategy of close collaboration between the Forest Service and the local population.

At the time of my first visit in 1986, the project had already been in operation for five years and was judged a success by most experts, although it was still too early to draw any firm conclusions.[10] During this second visit, however, on our previous day's journey from Kathmandu to Pokhara, I observed surprisingly few of the regular afforestation patterns which should have been evident everywhere if the project, now in its twelfth year, had really been such an outstanding success.

New Houses in a New Political Landscape

As we left the shade of the *chautara*, I could feel a certain tension mounting within me. Had the trees in Panchamool really flourished? Would I find that they had grown enough by now to constitute a forest? Or had they fallen victim to browsing livestock? At least the natural forest opposite the *chautara*, which belongs to Panchamool, was as thick with lofty sal trees as it had been seven years ago.

At first glance Sirubari seemed unchanged. But then I noticed that the temple had a new tower. New structures made of stone had taken the place of the old, oval-shaped Gurung dwellings with their mud walls and thatched roofs. The nation-wide political changes that had taken place since 1990 had also exerted an influence here: the unpopular *panchayat* committee and its administrators had been abolished and replaced by a newly established Village Development Committee. The democratically elected president of this new

committee, Hark Bahadur Gurung, now received us and offered us refreshments in the comfortable living-room of his stone house, while heavy rain started to pour down outside.

A New Forest Equal to 300 Playing Fields

The next morning the sky was as clear as if it had been freshly washed. People who had no urgent business gathered in front of Hark Bahadur's house, making it obvious that a considerable delegation would accompany us on our journey, just as on my last visit. Our route once again took us over carefully laid slabs of granite. It was not long before we entered the dominion of the forest spirits, a mysterious grove of mighty trees, clusters of bamboo and fallen rocks, eventually making our way along the lower border of the sacred protective forest. Here the ban on the use of forest resources was still respected, as I could verify from the remains of a fallen tree, which would have made good firewood but which was still lying undisturbed in the same place where I remembered having seen it on my previous visit.

The other side of the forest, however, where several dozen Kami families make their homes, appeared to be more vulnerable. The Kami belong to a low caste of blacksmiths. We could see a group of Kami women carrying baskets full of leaf litter across a small valley between the forest and their homes. They had obviously gathered the leaves despite the ban. Shrugging their shoulders, my companions explained that the relatively little land possessed by the Kami is not very fertile, so they are forced to compensate by fertilising it with large amounts of compost.

After a short while the first traces of the tree-planting campaign became evident in the form of individual specimens of *patle salla*, an exotic pine species from Mexico.[11] This tree had also been planted within the walls of the sacred protective forest. There, it provided a remarkable contrast to natural stands which contained *chilauna*, a tree-like relative of the tea bush; *katus*, a member of the chestnut family; and large rhododendrons, whose flowering time was just coming to an end.[12] Then, suddenly, I caught a glimpse of treetops at the site where planting had occured in the reforestation project. The trees themselves became gradually more visible as we continued to climb the granite steps. Reforestation had succeeded after all! The area originally covered by the project had since more than doubled in size, to 300 hectares.

Too Much Money, Too Little Time

The Community Forestry Development Project has unquestionably achieved its goal in Panchamool. Surprisingly, however, Panchamool is something of an exception in this regard. The high hopes aroused at the outset were only partially fulfilled by the early 1990s, even though by that time the project had absorbed the lion's share of the funds and the labour committed to forestry in Nepal for a number of years. The 1978 Forestry Act earmarked 1.8 million hectares – roughly half of the national forestland in Nepal – for use by the *panchayats*, yet only 4 per cent of this land was officially transferred by 1992.[13] As of 1990 a mere 35,000 hectares had been reforested, with Panchamool's portion constituting close to 1 per cent of this total.

Why did the project have such modest success? The answer to this question requires a closer look at the 1978 Forestry Act which was influenced in part by the Theory of Himalayan Environmental Degradation. In accordance with the terms of the act, the *panchayats* did not receive good forests; in most cases they were granted treeless or degraded forestland, on which trees were to be planted as thickly as possible in order to fulfil the aims of the project. Although tracts of forestland in this condition are considered degraded from the standpoint of classical forestry, they are not necessarily unproductive in the eyes of rural people, for whom the most important thing is that trees produce as many leaves as possible; it makes no

difference if their stems are short and crooked. But if areas like this are to be afforested, much hard work and years of waiting will be required before anything can be harvested. Consequently, unless forest resources have been heavily exhausted, an investment of this magnitude will not take place unless it is warranted by special circumstances.

Yet project efforts were fruitless even in many places where people would have been glad to have more trees. The most likely explanation for this lies in the realm of policy-making and administration. Despite its announced aims, the project rarely engaged people directly at the grass-roots level. Furthermore, it was far more generously endowed with money than with time – a fact which probably also made success more difficult to achieve.

Time is a crucial factor in the nurturing of trees. It also takes time to build up mutual trust and cooperation between the Forest Service and people at the local level. Villagers needed time simply to adjust to the change with which they were confronted when forestry officials, who had previously behaved like policemen, suddenly turned into development agents bearing armfuls of saplings. Meanwhile, the international donor community believed that the situation required urgent action. Alarmed by visions of the Himalayan foothills eroding away, donors made heavy investments of capital and pressed for quick results, expecting appropriate returns on their investment in the form of newly afforested land. As a result, pressure from above was felt throughout the ranks of the Forest Service. Obliged to meet goals set at the ministerial level, a district forest officer hardly had time to establish a sound working relationship with local people. Negotiations were invariably conducted with the *panchayat*, whose officials had no meaningful contacts with the grass-roots population and no contact at all with women, who are usually the direct users of forests in Nepal.

Most residents of Panchamool are Buddhists. The Hindus who live here frequently perform specific tasks and functions. The Kami, for instance, work as blacksmiths.

The Women's Club of Panchamool.
In the absence of men, who are
often away for decades, the
women are responsible for the
household and for agricultural
production. They also maintain
local infrastructure by doing
communal labour on paths and
check dams.

Box 3.1 Siva versus Kali

Erosion of catastrophic proportions occurs frequently in the Himalayas, owing to their recent geological origin. Tectonic forces are still at work on the Himalayan massif, which is being thrust upward by about one centimetre a year. As a result, rivers are cutting deeper into their channels, and mountainsides are sliding downwards. Earthquakes and landslides triggered by the infiltration of water from the monsoon rains both contribute a great deal of detritus to Himalayan rivers.[29]

According to Hindu legend, these catastrophic events are the work of Black Kali, the destructive consort of the god Siva. Although farmers in Nepal are powerless against Kali's fury, they are experts at controlling erosion on man-made cultural landscapes. Their experience is reflected in the broad range of expressions they use to describe and forecast events involving movement of the earth, such as cracks in the ground which foretell an impending landslide.[30] The well-maintained terraces they construct reduce the rate of erosion, especially if they are irrigated. Small-scale damage is repaired quickly, but even a cultural landscape that has sustained major damage is usually restored within a generation.[31]

The Theory of Himalayan Environmental Degradation must modify the blame it attaches to people living in the uplands for disasters which occur on the plains. Floods have been occurring since the time of the ancient Hindu Puranas, when even Siva's bountiful locks were incapable of calming Ganga's fury. (See Chapter 2 on India.)

Because he could not completely pacify either Ganga or Kali, Siva took consolation in transforming the catastrophes they wrought into something creative: disastrous landslides gave rise to fertile slopes on which agriculture could flourish once again, while floods that carried silt downhill produced the so-called 'golden soil' on the plains from which Bangladesh later took its name. Flood events became catastrophic only when humans began to live on the floodplains. This first occurred in association with the colonial plantation system. As populations continued to grow, more and more people came to inhabit the disaster-prone floodplains.

The people of Nepal are powerless against Black Kali, the goddess of destruction (right), when she appears in the form of earthquakes or violent monsoon rains that ravage the cultural landscape. But farmers such as Chandra Kumari (left), who lives in Panchamool, are unsurpassed when it comes to cleaning up and rebuilding in the wake of Kali's devastation.

Circumstances such as these illustrate how the inappropriate allocation of funds can have a disastrous effect. In many bilateral projects, such as those in which Nepal and Switzerland are partners, the costs of afforestation are estimated at 1500 rupees per hectare.[14] The project, however, spent 3500 rupees per hectare. This sum is the equivalent of one month's pay for a forest officer – an amount which neither allows him to live in a style befitting his rank nor to cover the expenses of educating his children. Given this situation, it is not surprising that the Forest Service had to take action against the misuse of CFDP funds in cases where forest officers conspired with *panchayat* functionaries to divert official funds into their own pockets.

The examples of Thokarpa and Panchamool notwithstanding, the project was largely unsuccessful in involving the general population. Because they possess herds of goats and are masters of the sickle, local people are in a position to decide the ultimate fate of virtually every sapling. Consequently, most of the millions of trees planted on *panchayat* land – in many cases with a great deal of effort – did not survive.

Education and the Autonomy of Women

To determine the reasons for the project's success in Panchamool, it is necessary to take a closer look at the social structure of the village. Panchamool has had a local school since 1929. In contrast to rural areas dominated by Hindus, it offers primary education not only to most of the boys in the village but also to the girls, who have been attending school here for decades. Furthermore, thanks to its mercenaries, the village has not only had a continual link to the outside world, but has also been confronted with issues of global concern, such as the growing threat posed by environmental problems. A local man returning home after decades of service abroad is relatively well-off and is also entitled to a pension. Many Gurung families can therefore afford solid stone houses,

and they have no need to gather every last leaf from the forest to feed their cattle or to fertilise their fields, since they have the means to purchase whatever they lack.

Religion and political history have had a great influence on life in Panchamool, and ultimately on afforestation as well. Pronounced differences exist between Hindus and Tibetan–Burmese peoples such as the Gurung. Gurung communities, for example, have enjoyed a great deal of local autonomy for centuries.[15] Buddhists such as the Gurung possess a strong sense of personal freedom, make conscious choices among various alternatives, and take initiative in altering the circumstances of their lives. Hindus, on the other hand, believe that human beings live out their lives as members of a particular caste, and that each individual must learn to endure the conditions of present existence. Hindu societies are therefore likely to be characterised by social hierarchy, fatalism and lethargy.[16] Although social differences exist in Panchamool, within the Buddhist community as well as between Buddhists and Hindus, they appear to be much less significant than in Kathmandu.

The women of Panchamool also enjoy greater autonomy and display more initiative than their Hindu sisters. Three years prior to my second visit, the Women's Club of Panchamool undertook the daunting task of meticulously constructing a wall several metres high to protect the local cremation site. A sense of community and a spirit of collaboration are also quite important here in other ways. This is reflected in Panchamool's carefully erected infrastructure, and in the arboretum and tea shop my hosts showed me near the nursery above the village. Here, on clear days, old soldiers sit gazing out over the Anapurna massif and tracts of land covered with trees which they planted themselves.

Better to Conserve One Tree than Plant Ten Saplings

After drinking a glass of hot buffalo milk, we

cannot be universally verified. Moreover, the extent to which upland populations are responsible for the water balance and for erosion must also be reexamined in light of recent evidence (see Box 3.1).

Empowering Local Communities to Ensure a Better Future

Modifying the Theory of Himalayan Environmental Degradation is not the same as saying that there are no problems in the Himalayas. Viewing these problems in relative terms can, however, have the effect of ameliorating the seemingly harsh inevitability of degradation, while also leading to new problem-solving approaches and allowing time to implement them. In addition, positive findings in recent years have rehabilitated the reputation of the people living in the mountains of Nepal, and have demonstrated, above all, that they are capable of caring for their environment, so long as they encounter no obstacles in their efforts at self-organisation.

For a long time Nepal did not have social and political conditions that were conducive to local autonomy. Political conditions only became more favourable with the popular uprising of 1990. The new constitution of the same year proclaimed democracy and decentralisation of political power, as well as an end to the exploitation of individuals and entire social classes, and promised equitable distribution of revenues obtained from the country's natural resources. And the five-year plan for the period of 1992–1997 emphasises popular sovereignty and the right of the people to implement their decisions.[24]

Decentralisation is also the guiding principle of the 1993 Forestry Act, which is considered one of the most innovative and progressive of its kind. This law stipulates that control of Nepal's mountain forests – and not merely tracts with virtually no trees, as during the *panchayat* era – should be transferred to the local population, provided that they organise themselves into communities of users. These user groups would also receive all revenues from forest products. A community of users in this context no longer refers to villages or even to entire *panchayats*, but to small user groups which have always managed more or less clearly defined tracts of local forestland. Though the forest will legally remain the property of the state, the new management plan, which the Forest Service must elaborate in cooperation with each user group, guarantees rights of use to local people over the long term. Decisions are to be made jointly by all individuals who enjoy rights of use – especially women – and revenues are to be shared equally.

Technically, the main focus of the new law is no longer on afforestation but on management of the surviving natural forests. New plantations will play an important role only on heavily degraded or eroded soil, in places where there are no trees, or where desirable species no longer grow naturally. The underlying principles of the 1993 Forestry Act stand in diametrical opposition to long-established gender roles, the hierarchical social structure in Nepal, and the country's highly centralised form of government. It will therefore come as no surprise if it takes decades to implement these principles as it once took decades to initiate a comparable process in the Swiss Alps.

The Need for a New Generation of Foresters

Forestry officials will have to be committed to reform if the new law is to succeed. Experience to the mid 1990s has been mixed. Forest wardens vary in their ability to commit themselves to new and creative partnerships with local people. Some have experienced the transfer of control over the forests as a loss of power and status, and perhaps even as a threat to their professional existence. This makes them more likely to prevent rather than to promote the establishment of user groups. Yet, if experience in the Alps is any guide, the Forest Service in Nepal will have more than enough to do for quite a long time to come.

The first stage alone – resolving internal

The same white sandalwood tree in the reforested area above Sirubari, shortly after it was planted in 1986 (above), and seven years later (middle). The effects of reforestation in Panchamool in 1993 (below).

Tanzania

A Second Garden of Eden

The Chagga originally settled long ago on the fertile slopes of Mount Kilimanjaro. As their habitat became increasingly restricted, first by colonisation and later by rapid population growth, the Chagga were forced to increase their agricultural productivity and to grow a wider variety of crops. They accomplished this primarily by making better use of space both above and below the soil. The ultimate result was an array of multistoreyed tree gardens, which are among the most fully developed of their kind and comprise a model agroforestry system. The wealth of different species these gardens contain helps to ensure both ecological and economic sustainability even in times of crisis, such as Tanzania has experienced in recent decades.

Box 4.1 Water: the vital resource

Kilimanjaro's most valuable product is not its coffee but its water, which supplies a considerable part of northern Tanzania. In addition to rain and snow, 'horizontal precipitation' – moisture which is 'combed out' of the clouds passing through the forest belt – also plays a role in determining the available water supply.[42] Mosses and lichens, found most frequently at altitudes between 2200 and 4400 metres, directly above the fertile lands inhabited by the Chagga, are particularly efficient collectors of water.[43]

In recent years there has been less discharge in a number of Tanzania's rivers, especially during the dry season between July and October. There are several probable reasons for this:

- Clear-cutting and subsequent planting of cypresses and pines on the western slope of Kilimanjaro has resulted in single-storeyed monocultures which are less efficient water collectors than multi storeyed natural forests. Moreover, mosses and lichens grow sparsely on these exotic species; this is one of many reasons why preference should be given to the cultivation of indigenous species.
- The spread of agricultural land to steep slopes and deforestation along streams have reduced storage capacity in the ground. Precipitation drains away more rapidly, increasing erosion along stream channels and banks.
- The Chagga have been consuming increasing amounts of water owing to population growth and the expansion of agriculture. Legal water use alone has quadrupled in the last 40 years.[44]

forward as justification for colonising Africa, the real driving forces behind colonisation were industrialists, merchants and bankers; it was they who prodded their governments to embark on a quest for raw materials and new markets.[6] Colonies, as the German explorer Carl Peters bluntly put it, were needed to advance the fortunes of profit-making enterprises in the mother country.[7]

The partitioning of Africa by the European colonial powers, the United States, and the Ottoman Empire began in earnest at the Berlin Conference of 1885. A year later Germany and Britain established areas of influence in East Africa. Present-day Tanzania, minus the island of Zanzibar, became German East Africa, while Kenya, which lay immediately to the north, became a British protectorate.[8]

In 1895 colonial administrators officially nationalised all the territory in German East Africa, enclosing common lands to create a system of private property. Extensive areas of land on the lower ridges of Kilimanjaro, which had long been cultivated by different clans, were assigned to colonial enterprises, missionary societies and white settlers.[9] Hut taxes

Water from Mount Kilimanjaro is a valuable national resource. The Chagga have long tapped water from the mountain for their settlements; among other things, this has made it possible for them to stable their cattle.

The marketplace in Machame,
where onions and plantains
used for cooking and brewing
beer are for sale.

Kenya

'Women Under the Acacia Tree':
Solidarity in the Face of Drought
and Hunger

The Kitui district of Kenya, where
it is extremely dry for much of the
year, is exposed to harsh climatic
conditions which affect half of the
African continent. As a result of
drought and crop failures, the
people of Kitui are forced to secure
a livelihood by any means at their
disposal. The impressive role played
by women in the struggle for
survival here is made possible only
by their firm commitment to
solidarity. One example is 'Women
Under the Acacia Tree', a group
formed by women in Kitui who
operate nurseries where they raise
local tree species. Because trees not
only supply traditional products but
also help to maintain soil fertility,
they are practically as important as
drinking water in this semi-arid
climate. Yet agroforestry systems
like the ones which have long
existed in fertile tropical highland
areas are only in the early stages of
development here.

Costa Rica

Managing Secondary Forests to Preserve Primary Forests

In recent decades Costa Rica has lost large tracts of its tropical primary (old growth) forests, which were cleared mainly to pave the way for speculative cattle breeding and cash crops grown for export. Much of the cleared area has since proven unsuitable for these purposes, however, and trees have begun to grow again on abandoned grazing areas. The resulting secondary forests will not only play an important role in supplying timber and other forest products in future, but also in preserving biodiversity. As wood becomes increasingly scarce and prices rise, secondary forests offer the additional advantage of providing landless subsistence farmers with a chance to earn income. This opportunity will have to be exploited if pressure on remaining primary forest reserves and national parks is to be reduced.

'*Mira, este lindo Laurelito!*' Thrilled by the sight of the slim little tree he was indicating with the tip of his machete, Rafael Gamboa cleared away the thick weeds that had surrounded it with two swift strokes. *Laurelito* is a pet name for the laurel, a remarkable tree found extensively throughout the tropical Americas. When fully mature, a laurel tree can produce hundreds of thousands of seeds which are scattered widely by the wind. Wherever a gap appears in the dense canopy of the rainforest, laurel seeds are sure to germinate once again before long.[1]

Don Rafael, who was born in 1927, eventually grew tall, just like his beloved *Laurelito*. His face now shows the weathered effects of life as a campesino, and his hand seems to grip the machete like a claw. He lives in a house seven kilometres outside the village of Siquirres, where the Cordillera central mountain range descends to the Atlantic coastal plain. More than 4000 millimetres of annual rainfall, distributed evenly throughout the year, give this area a tropical humid climate. Don Rafael cultivates a 13-hectare *finca* on which he raises maize, cassava, fruits and vegetables for home consumption, and bananas, coffee, cocoa and cattle for the market. He also sells timber from his own forest, which begins immediately behind his house.

Don Rafael's forest began to grow spontaneously 30 years ago, after grazing was abandoned. As secondary forest, it is markedly different from the primary forest that Don Rafael's father once cleared from the same land, both in terms of its species and its structure. Roughly 25 different species of trees developed naturally here, among which laurel, *Guacimo blanco* (a relative of linden) and *Anonillo* are the best established.[2] These species are well suited for furniture-making and are also good sources of plywood; their wood currently commands a good price. Don Rafael has observed trees all his life and is well acquainted with different species and how they grow. His *Laurelito*, for example, grew hip-high within a few months. Another laurel tree nearby had a stem as big as that of a 15-year-old European beech tree,

although it was only three years old.

Rafael Gamboa's knowledge of the forest is the basis of his special relationship with trees. He loves his trees and speaks tenderly of them. At the same time, he is aware of their economic value; he knows they are a kind of 'capital' that earns 'interest' in the form of wood. Trees are better than money in the bank, especially nowadays when Costa Rica is one of the countries where wood is becoming noticeably scarcer.

The Vital Role of Wood in Villa Mills

Wood also plays an important role in the life of Donato Abarca, who lives in Villa Mills, a commune in the Cordillera de Talamanca about 60 kilometres south-west of Rafael Gamboa's home. The Talamanca mountains rise like a gigantic saurian crest between the Atlantic and

Previous page: The cattle boom triggered by the 'hamburger connection' in the 1960s is the major cause of widespread deforestation in Costa Rica in recent decades. Pastures are increasingly being extended to steeper land with heavier rainfall where the risk of erosion is greater.

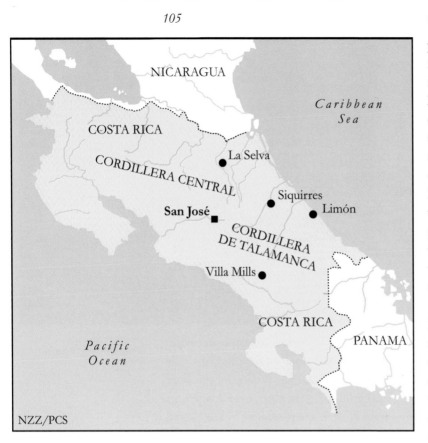

NICARAGUA

*Caribbean
Sea*

COSTA RICA

CORDILLERA CENTRAL

• La Selva

Siquirres
■ San José   •
• Limón

CORDILLERA
DE TALAMANCA

Villa Mills •

COSTA RICA

*Pacific
Ocean*

PANAMA

NZZ/PCS

produce charcoal at the age of eight. Now over 50 years old and still a *carbonero*, he shows the fatigue that comes from rising early and working long hours. Don Donato is in a much less comfortable position than Rafael Gamboa. Charcoal provides an increasingly meagre source of income, because cooking is now done either electrically or with gas in many towns. Demand comes only from the well-to-do, who want charcoal for barbecuing, and from the poor, at the other end of the social spectrum, who need it to prepare *gallo pinto*, rice served with black beans, which is the Costa Rican national dish.

Charcoal producers have also encountered legal problems. Villa Mills is part of the largest remaining expanse of primary mountain rainforest in Costa Rica. In order to protect this environment, which includes tracts of forest-land that have traditionally been used by village-dwellers, the Rio Macho Forest Reserve was established in the mid 1970s. Timber harvesting is forbidden in the reserve, so the *carboneros* are allowed to burn only dead trees. Moreover, Don Donato has also had bad luck with his *finca*. Although he claimed the land surrounding his home long ago, he was unwilling to sacrifice the three sacks of charcoal necessary to finance the trip to the land registry office. Hence he did not obtain clear title to his property in time. Today most of his land lies within the boundaries of the Rio Macho Reserve, which means that he no longer has a chance to sell it. Don Donato, who now suffers from rheumatism, will probably be unable to fulfil his dream of owning a *finca* in a more favourable climate 'where everything flourishes'.

In Villa Mills alone, dozens of *carboneros* are caught in the same economic trap as Donato Abarca: their chances of earning a livelihood here are limited. The climate is too wet for crops or even for livestock. Without access to wood, life at this altitude becomes difficult, even for the young. Children here often help their fathers split oak logs virtually from the time they are able to walk. With the little education they receive, these young people are

Pacific coastal plains. Villa Mills lies at an altitude of 2700 metres above sea level, where the climate is wet and frequently cool. Here the Atlantic trade winds bring a steady stream of humid air which condenses when it hits the mountains. Thick cloud cover can develop from midday onwards, and rain is frequent.

The natural vegetation at this altitude is mountain rainforest. Because they are often shrouded in clouds, the oak trees which dominate the landscape here form what are known as 'oak cloud forests', or elfin forests, because of the fairy-tale atmosphere they create.[3] Each tree, which can grow as high as 50 metres, is truly a world unto itself, thickly adorned with orchids, bromelias, ferns, mosses and other epiphytes.

The area that includes Villa Mills was first settled in the 1940s, when the *Interamericana* road which links Alaska and Patagonia was built. It was at this time that Donato Abarca's father came here as a labourer. He soon abandoned road construction work, however, having discovered that he could earn a better living from charcoal. Donato himself began to help

Rafael Gamboa and his wife (above, left); Donato Abarca, the carbonero (below, left).

ill equipped for life in the city. The inhabitants of Villa Mills are thus left with virtually no alternative but to take what they need from the oak forest when they cannot obtain timber by legal means.

From Coffee to Hamburger Meat

Although Costa Rica is a democratically governed country with an emerging economy and the best educational system and the highest per capita income in the region, many of its people still find themselves in an even more precarious economic position than the *carboneros* of Villa Mills. The marginal lives they are forced to lead, and their plundering of forest resources, constitute the downside of the modern Costa Rican economic model, which is based on the export of largely unprocessed agricultural products.

The name 'Costa Rica' is said to go back to Columbus, who received gifts of gold from the indigenous Indians when he became the first European to set foot on Central American soil near Limon in 1502.[4] Yet the so-called 'rich coast' fell far short of delivering what it seemed to promise: the land proved to be poor in mineral resources, and even the potential of its rich volcanic soils could not be exploited at first because most of the indigenous population had fallen victim either to the Spanish conquistadores or the diseases they brought to the New World. Consequently, extensive feudal landholding systems, such as those in Mexico and Guatemala, which were based on forced labour performed by a subjugated indigenous population, never became established in Costa Rica. A more equitable structure of ownership developed instead, where even colonial governors were long obliged to plant maize and beans with their own hands.

Early attempts to export cocoa and tobacco failed, owing to raids carried out by the English pirates who haunted the Caribbean. But thanks to coffee, a transition from subsistence agriculture to an export-based economy was underway by the mid nineteenth century. Rich in humus, the volcanic soils of the Valle Central

'Oak cloud forests' near Villa Mills (right); the forest floor (above).

around San José were ideal for the coffee bush.

Coffee was not destined to remain the only successful crop, however, as demand for other 'colonial products' soon rose in the prosperous countries of Europe as well as in the United States. At the beginning of the twentieth century, this demand was met by bananas, which were first planted not far from Rafael Gamboa's *finca*. It was at this point that land ownership on a large scale was first seen in Costa Rica. The predecessors of America's United Fruit Company, for example, received extensive tracts of land in exchange for completing the 'jungle train' which linked San José with Limon until 1989.[5]

Three-quarters of Costa Rica was still covered with forest at the end of World War II, yet fires set to clear the land for agriculture soon began to blaze with increasing frequency.[6] Following the Cuban Revolution in 1959, the United States sought new sources of sugar cane, and in the 1960s the rapid development of the American fast food industry was responsible for the 'hamburger connection' – the most ominous development of all. The pressure to supply fast food outlets led to a shortage of inexpensive meat in the United States, but lean meat could still be purchased cheaply in Central America. As demand rose, extensive areas of forest in Costa Rica were converted to grazing land. Beef exports, which

Experience in recent decades has shown that sustainable management of open areas in the rainforests of Costa Rica is possible only to a limited extent. Shown here are three alternatives to livestock production and the deforestation linked with it: Secondary forests, which produce non-timber forest products such as medicinal plants, natural pesticides and decorative plants, in addition to timber (above, with the broad-leaved pioneer guarumo); agroforestry systems, with cacao (below, left); and coffee (below, right). Tree gardens such as these are initially highly susceptible to erosion, especially if they are established over extensive areas on steep terrain.

stood at 8000 tonnes in 1960, rose to 5.5 times this amount by 1977.[7]

Agricultural Frontiers

The export of non-processed foods left Costa Rica brutally exposed to price fluctuations in the global market. When prices dropped, landowners at the bottom of the economic scale were the first to feel the pinch: the smallest producers to survive each successive crisis were usually already so heavily in debt that selling their *finca* was the only option open to them. This brought about significant social restructuring, as fewer and fewer people came to possess more and more of the best land. This process of social change, which began in the 1930s, is still continuing today.

In Costa Rica the forest has traditionally served as a buffer to cushion the effects of hard times. People who lost their land and became *precaristas* could always ease their precarious situation by clearing a patch of forest, which they could at least use to ward off hunger. Since the 1950s agricultural frontiers have appeared wherever new roads are built. Concentrated land use and the high rate of population growth at this time played a significant role in this process. Subsequently, in the 1970s and 1980s, many people living at the margins of society migrated to the towns. Nevertheless, the agricultural frontiers remained the scene of much activity owing to civil wars in Nicaragua and El Salvador, which forced hundreds of thousands of refugees to flee to Costa Rica.

While trees have played a central role in the economy of the indigenous Amerindian population, here since time immemorial, Costa Ricans of Spanish descent have traditionally regarded the forest as an obstacle. It is hard to find people like Rafael Gamboa, who can spend the entire day in peaceful contemplation beneath his trees until he is suddenly surprised by nightfall. The traditional attitude towards forests is summed up by the expression *Conquista de la Selva*, which implies that the forest is a world inhabited by snakes, mosquitoes and Indians.

Trees are regarded as weeds, and allowing them to stand is a sign of laziness. Anyone who 'improves' the land by clearing it has the right to claim title to it. Moreover, until recently, Costa Rican law provided that forestland was taxed at a higher rate than cleared land.[8]

Capital Lays a Stronger Claim to the Forest than Hunger

The cattle boom had a major impact on Costa Rica. Because clear-cutting took place on an increasingly larger scale, starting in the 1960s, the pace of deforestation accelerated and social disparities became even greater. Despite this, alleviating hunger was not the main reason for clearing land; large tracts were now converted to rangeland at the whim of those who commanded substantial amounts of capital, which they sought to invest as profitably as possible.

The *precaristas* have always been at the cutting edge of events. Many of them live in such uncertain circumstances that they are prepared to sell the land they have spent great effort to clear as soon as a rancher offers to buy it. Others work for cattle barons in exchange for permission to cultivate food crops for two or three years. This has the effect of pushing the agricultural frontier ever deeper into the forest, onto increasingly steeper slopes where rainfall is heavier and there is a continual danger of erosion. Converting forests to rangeland makes good economic sense in light of the prevailing economic and legal conditions in Costa Rica. In addition to being the basis of meat production, cattle can also be financed with credit offered on favourable terms. At the same time, ranching is a way of satisfying the desire to speculate in land. Cattle serve as live boundary markers which define the borders of private property.[9] They are a source of stable production in a hazardous environment, and they also represent cultural identity and confer social status. The Inter-American Development Bank and the World Bank have both promoted beef production in Costa Rica by supplying credit for slaughterhouses.[10] Farmers who own no cattle and produce only for home consumption and the local market have no chance of receiving credit.

By the 1990s, rangelands had expanded to cover 35 to 40 per cent of Costa Rica, a development which had disastrous consequences for the national economy. A head of cattle needs a grazing area the size of a soccer field; half a tonne of forest biomass must first be burned off to produce a single hamburger.[11] Forest cover has now been reduced to one third of the country's total area; 35,000 hectares disappeared annually between 1970 and 1990 alone.

However, already at the end of the 1980s there was a sudden collapse in demand for beef because a large fast-food chain in the US, which had been the target of a boycott, subsequently abandoned meat imports from Costa Rica. State-owned banks were forced to write off credits in excess of 100 million US dollars. However, in view of the estimated 50 million US dollars worth of fertile topsoil that is annually washed away to the sea, it is clear that a far higher price has been paid in ecological terms.[12]

In addition, a great deal of wildlife as well as vast quantities of non-woody vegetation were destroyed by the advancing agricultural frontier. Because it is a land bridge that connects North and South America, Costa Rica is endowed with particularly rich biodiversity. More than 800 species of birds and 12,000 plants can be found here; approximately 1400 of the latter can be classified as trees, in stark contrast to Central Europe which has only 50 different species of trees.[13] Now, however, many of the country's plant and animal species are threatened by the rapid disappearance of their natural habitat.

Although the pace of destruction slowed somewhat with the drop in demand for meat, uncertainty about the market for exports has continued to expose the economic disadvantages of monocultures. When a huge demand for tropical fruit emerged in Eastern Europe in the early 1990s after the fall of the Berlin Wall, thousands of hectares of forest along the Atlantic Coast were converted into new plantations. Many subsistence farmers sold their land to banana producers and hired

themselves out as plantation hands. Costa Rica became the world's second most important producer of bananas, with over 80 million cartons annually; this sector of the economy provided 50,000 jobs and was responsible for one quarter of the income derived from exports.[14] Yet the first fruit had hardly ripened when the European Union, in defiance of the General Agreement on Tariffs and Trade (GATT), decided in 1993 to limit the importation of 'dollar' bananas from Latin America. This resulted in production cutbacks, unemployment and a new class of *precaristas*; the agricultural frontiers came alive once again, and smoke could be seen everywhere.

The Wrong Diagnosis Leads to the Wrong Treatment

During the course of the cattle boom the timber industry played only a secondary role in deforestation. Rather than paving the way by opening up the forests themselves, timber interests in Costa Rica tended to operate in the wake of those who cleared the land (for a contrasting development, see Chapter 7 on Indonesia). Ninety per cent of the timber cleared – 10 to 16 million cubic metres annually between 1963 and 1989 – was either burned off or left to rot, representing an overall economic loss of several billion dollars.[15]

For a long time it seemed that wood was a resource as inexhaustible in Costa Rica as oil appears to be in industrialised countries. Because prices were low, even for precious woods, hardly anyone who owned land had an incentive to preserve forests, let alone manage them sustainably. Clear-cutting was seen as an investment rather than as a liquidation of capital in the form of wood. In the process, no notice was taken when surpluses suddenly disappeared and wood became scarce. The fact that scarcity was not signalled by rising prices was probably due primarily to the regulations governing timber harvesting, which had long been regarded as the main cause of deforestation. The resulting mass of new regulations made it necessary to spend days applying for legal permission to fell a tree.

Surreptitious plundering of the
forest is frequently the only means
of survival for people in precarious
economic circumstances.

Owing to these complications, it was virtually impossible to export wood. Therefore, as no demand was created, there was no established price for Costa Rican timber on the world market.

A similar impact resulted from the refusal of American and European banana importers to accept the pallets on which banana cartons were stacked and shipped because they were made of tropical wood. This move was motivated by the fear of a boycott of bananas. Costa Rica is now forced to import 12 million US dollars worth of wooden pallets annually from the North.[16] In addition, there is currently no incentive for farmers to grow laurel or other appropriate species. What Karl Kasthofer concluded about Alpine forests in the nineteenth century appears to hold true for the tropical forests of Costa Rica as well: trees disappear rapidly because their wood has no real economic value. It makes more sense in economic terms to convert the forests to other purposes.

Saving the Forests

As the destruction of tropical forests continued, pressure to conserve them began to mount, and numerous technical measures were put forward. As early as the 1950s, tree gardens such as those used on Mount Kilimanjaro were proposed for Costa Rica.[17] Meanwhile, different agroforestry systems were established, including coffee planted with *poro* trees and cocoa grown beneath laurel trees.[18] A great deal of agroforestry research is currently being done in Costa Rica, with dozens of different plant combinations being tested.[19]

The first nature reserves were set aside in the 1960s and 1970s; by the mid 1990s almost one quarter of the total area of Costa Rica was subject to some form of protection. The aim is to conserve enough of each of the different types of natural habitat to prevent loss of biodiversity. To keep them from becoming isolated islands, reserves are linked by corridors of protective forest such as the *paseo pantera* ('panther promenade'). This is also the basic principle of reserves which extend across national boundaries, such as the La Amistad Reserve, a portion of which is in Panama. National parks are important, and not only for ecological reasons. Well over half a million tourists visit Costa Rica each year, and four-fifths of them come primarily to experience the beauty of the country's natural landscape. By the early 1990s, 'ecotourism' was the second most important source of foreign exchange, behind bananas and ahead of coffee.[20]

Trees die even in oak cloud forests. As long as forest management simulates the dynamics of nature and felling takes place selectively and does not exceed the natural capacity for growth and regeneration, neither forest structure nor composition will be significantly altered. Important criteria for sustainable forestry will therefore be fulfilled.

Large-scale reforestation projects, begun in the late 1980s, were made possible by state subsidies. The projects were often ineffective, however, as the trees used were not appropriate to the site, and seed quality and care were both inadequate. Reforestation efforts were frequently launched by large investment groups, which took advantage of state subsidies and then abandoned newly planted tracts to their own fate. In some cases natural forests were cleared so that exotic species could be planted in their place.[21]

Finally, in recent years increased attention has been given to sustainable management of natural forests, a comprehensive approach to forest preservation. Natural forest management already has a long history in Costa Rica, dating back to 1953, when Leslie Holdridge, a far-sighted American expert on tropical forests, bought the *Finca La Selva* in Sarapiquí in order to experiment with different silvicultural approaches that would conserve forests and allow them to regenerate naturally.[22]

Rapid Growth and Early Death

There is a belief in industrialised countries that tropical forests cannot regenerate after trees have been cut down, even when cutting is selective. Timber felling is generally linked with subsequent severe erosion. But severe degradation only occurs in extreme cases, as when heavy machinery causes soil compaction.[23] Moreover, tropical vegetation exhibits extraordinary regenerative powers (see Box 6.1).

The reaction of the ecosystem to disturbances is virtually the same everywhere in the rainforests of the Central and South American lowlands. When crown cover is destroyed on a large scale as the result of storms or clear-cutting, pioneer species such as *balsa* or *guarumo*, whose wood is soft and non-durable, are frequently the first species to become reestablished.[24] They grow very rapidly and quickly cover the forest floor with gigantic leaves. During their short, intense lifespan of several decades, these species absorb a good portion of the nutrients released by burning and decomposition. After these pioneers perish

Box 6.1 Even tropical forests can regenerate

Little information is currently available on processes of succession and growth in tropical forests. One of the most complete databanks compiled in the American tropics is a series of measurements made by the Swiss forester Jean-Pierre Veillon in Venezuela in the 1950s. Veillon regularly recorded data on trees, using the same sample for approximately 30 years. In the eastern plains of Venezuela, a part of the Orinoco watershed, Veillon's data, interpreted in the light of subsequent historical research, have provided astounding insight into the dynamics of vegetation in tropical dry forests.

It was discovered that in this region agriculture flourished up to 1810, after which the region was depopulated owing to various wars of liberation as well as civil wars. Forests then reestablished themselves on fields and pastureland, doubling in area by 1950.[46] These secondary forests were rich in valuable wood such as mahogany and cedar, which had proliferated greatly. The same development took place in the last century in Yucatan, where numerous wars also paved the way for nature to take its course.[47]

and decay, they become a source of nutrients for the trees that succeed them.

The pioneers are followed by the types of trees that Rafael Gamboa grows, which take seed while the short-lived pioneers are flourishing and grow in their shade. Because they also adapt to growing conditions in gaps left by individual trees, these trees are known as 'gap opportunists.' They grow relatively quickly and have a life expectancy of about 100 years. Only an expert can distinguish between a primary forest and a secondary forest composed of these species. Primary (old growth) forests constitute the third phase of tree succession. Primary forest first

Ian Hutchinson (right), an expert on secondary forests. Hutchinson's silvicultural visions of favouring high-quality trees become reality with the help of Don Adriel's skilfully applied chainsaw (left).

structure nor existing species are significantly affected in the process. Thus the conditions necessary for the protection of biodiversity can be maintained.

The economic benefits derived from these experiments are also satisfactory, with yields far greater than what the *carboneros* earn by their own efforts. Because their cutting is illegal, *carboneros* are forced to burn valuable timber in order to claim that their charcoal is produced from dead wood. In the CATIE project, however, the best timber was sold to sawmills, while timber of lower quality was sold for fenceposts. Only wood from the crowns of the trees was used to produce charcoal. The total proceeds not only covered harvest costs but also the cost of construction for a permanent logging road, confirming the economic sustainability of this approach. Most of the work was done by Donato Abarca's son Alvaro and five young colleagues. They helped to construct the logging road and the skidder tracks leading to the experimental plots. With training, they became experts in the use of chainsaws, which was verified by the small amount of damage caused during cutting.[41]

The CATIE experiments, conducted on approximately 20 hectares, not only provided legitimate employment for several young inhabitants of Villa Mills but also gave them a new outlook on life. Yet social sustainability – a prerequisite for sustainable resource use and

long-term preservation of oak forests – will only be achieved if every family dependent on timber is involved in the effort. As owner of the forest, the state has two options. It can conduct forestry operations itself – providing permanent employment on approximately 1000 hectares for most of the men of Villa Mills – or it can hand over the same amount of land for communal use by the *carboneros*. The commune of Villa Mills could then draw up a management plan in cooperation with the forest service. The forest service would be responsible for overseeing execution of the plan and monitoring forest growth. The plan could be modified according to unforeseen developments. Well motivated, the community could control internal violations and also prevent plundering by outsiders. This would create a buffer zone along an exposed section of the *Interamericana* highway, and protect the core area of the forest reserve.

Inspiring *Precaristas* to Become Conservationists

Buffer zones must also be established around the remaining lowland forests. Here it may be necessary to sacrifice a tract of primary forest in order to protect the core. Recent experience has shown that agriculture can only be sustained to a limited extent on open land at lowland sites with heavy rainfall. Sustainable agriculture instead will

Part of Rafael Gamboa's secondary forest, with 15-20-year-old laurel trees (above, right).

require trees, either as part of an agroforestry system or in the form of a forest. But putting such knowledge into practice on the frontier of slash-and-burn agriculture will require a great effort at every level.

Both Rafael Gamboa's private forest and the experiments carried out by CATIE demonstrate that sustainable forest management is technically possible as well as profitable, even under current conditions.[42] Secondary forests also represent great economic potential in terms of non-timber forest products, such as medicinal plants, natural pesticides, fibres and ornamental plants.[43] Agroforestry research is now focusing closely on subsistence farmers and *precaristas* who often try to eke out an existence using only a hoe. Land tenure laws have also been modified: legal title to land can now be obtained in exchange for conserving the forest.[44]

However, here, as in other places, technical solutions alone will not be enough. The hope expressed in the slogan '*Planta arboles, planta esperanza*' will only be realised if the social and economic situation of marginal people is improved. Numerous non-governmental organisations are currently making efforts in this direction. They are in a better position than government officials to see things through the eyes of local populations and to support local people until they can determine for themselves just what 'development' means to them. By working together, non-governmental organisations can also successfully oppose the interests of traditional elites and put pressure on politicians.

Legal security is of paramount importance to *precaristas* and subsistence farmers. Most people in these categories need support to overcome the administrative obstacles they face in recording title to their land. In addition, the cultivation of trees requires a great deal of advice and assistance, from far-sighted planning to support for marketing operations. The sooner the *precaristas* realise that wood can constitute a major source of their family income, the better protected they will be against the uncertainty of global market forces. And many of them will care for their trees as carefully as Rafael Gamboa does.

Indonesia

A Stable Cultural Landscape Based on Resin

In Krui, on the west coast of Sumatra, the entire landscape is marked by one natural product – resin – which is collected and sold for use in the production of varnish and batik fabrics. Resin-producing trees grow on steep hillsides, above valleys covered with rice fields. This is a cultural landscape which displays remarkable stability, both economically and ecologically. Resin provides regular income, and the rivers here remain clear and unmuddied by erosion run-off, even after heavy downpours. The land-use system in Krui could well serve as an example for other rainforest regions, such as vast areas of Sumatra and Borneo where forests have been destroyed in recent decades.

Rather than clearing small patches, as indigenous residents have traditionally done, recent settlers extend the agricultural frontier with slash-and-burn techniques on a broad front. Burning on a large scale is often motivated by the desire for profit. Government management of forests disrupted traditional local forms of resource use, while leaving the state unable to exert its control over extensive areas. The result was a virtual no-man's land where exploitation took place as the result of speculative agricultural ventures such as pepper cultivation.

and South America, where trees which produce valuable timber are widely scattered, marketable species grow close together in South-East Asia. Concession fees and export taxes on timber were much lower in Indonesia than in places such as the part of Borneo that belonged to Malaysia. For the first ten or 12 years, profits made by timber enterprises were correspondingly higher, sometimes amounting to half the invested capital in a single year.[25] The timber boom peaked at the end of the 1970s. Within just ten years, Indonesia's share of total global exports of tropical wood had risen from 0 to over 40 per cent, exceeding that of Africa and Latin America combined.[26] The lion's share of the timber exported from Indonesia was shipped unprocessed to Japan, which had become the site of the world's largest timber 'black hole'. Between 1970 and 1985 half of all global timber exports went to Japan – including tropical hardwoods from South-East Asia and great quantities of coniferous trees from North America.[27] One branch of the timber industry important to the local economy in Japan is the processing of raw wood to make paper, plywood and other products, some of which are subsequently exported.

Japan is also the world's leading consumer of wood per capita. Much of the country's timber imports are used in the manufacture of non-durable products such as concrete casings and *waribashi* – disposable chopsticks whose production requires hundreds of tonnes of wood daily.[28]

A Story of Plunder

The aim of Indonesia's forest policy was always to process domestic timber within the country rather than export it. Consequently, agreements with timber contractors stipulated that they must establish sawmills within the first five years of their operations, and plywood factories during a second five-year period. Very few contractors adhered to these conditions, however. Many objected that the 20-year duration of their contracts was too short to justify such high investments. In reality, most contractors – even domestically financed Indonesian firms – were fortune-hunters. This was reflected in their names: *Kayu Mas* ('golden wood') or *Sumber Mas* ('fountain of gold'). These firms were interested in using their concessions to 'skim' the best trees as quickly as possible, and rampant exploitation was the order of the day.[29] Almost half of the trees left standing were damaged by careless logging procedures or scraped by the steel tracks of caterpillars. As more daylight began to penetrate the forest, it created favourable conditions for lianas, which grew in thick bunches as they climbed and eventually killed the damaged trees.[30]

There were far too few foresters to control this situation. Still, even foresters inclined to halt the wanton exploitation of the forests would have received little support from their superiors. Taxes imposed on felling were the main source of income for the provinces, and many forestry officials also managed to divert some of the proceeds for themselves.[31] In 1983 the Ministry of Forestry in Jakarta discovered that provincial authorities had already granted or promised timber concessions totalling 1.5 million hectares more than the ministry had reserved for production forests.[32]

The timber boom eventually collapsed in the early 1980s, after the national government doubled export taxes. Felling operations temporarily dropped off sharply. Since exports of processed wood were still untaxed, however, timber concerns were now induced to construct sawmills and plywood factories. The Japanese bowed to the inevitable and joined together with Indonesian partners to build up the domestic timber industry. Europeans and Americans, on the other hand, had completely abandoned their timber operations in Indonesia by the mid 1980s.

Settlers Along the Logging Trails Transform the Landscape

The departure of these timber contractors made it easier to see the extent to which other forces had begun to gnaw away at the forests of Kalimantan and Sumatra. Timber-felling had brought a far-reaching process of transformation in its wake, whose driving force was centred in the densely populated islands of Indonesia's interior. The population of Java, for example, doubled to approximately 100 million between 1950 and 1980. Since two-thirds of this population was landless, many people emigrated with the hope of obtaining land of their own or finding work. Migrants first went to Sumatra, where the soils are relatively fertile, and later to the booming island of Kalimantan.

At the same time, it was official government policy from the beginning of the twentieth century to resettle people from Java on Indonesia's sparsely populated outer islands. Some one million people were 'transmigrated' during the 1970s, which amounted to no more than one-twentieth of the increase in the population of Java during the same period. There were plans to resettle an additional one million families during the 1980s. At a cost of 10,000 US dollars per household since the mid 1980s, this meant that the government had budgeted more money for the *projek transmigrasi* than it spent for health care and family planning during the same period.[33] This official resettlement programme was open to criticism for reasons other than its ineffectiveness and its high costs, however. In Kalimantan, projects which were carried out in regions with fertile soil, where local populations had long been established, became a source of ongoing conflicts over land.[34] Many new settlements were poorly planned and located at sites where the soil was poor and the water supply was a problem, so that Javanese rice farmers were unable to establish their traditional *sawah*.

Most of the new settlers on these outlying islands – both those who had emigrated voluntarily and those who had been resettled by the government – had no choice but to support themselves by slash-and-burn agriculture. As the Javanese were not experienced in the use of fire to clear land, however, they created *ladang* that were much too large for the two to four hectares allotted to them, and they were soon forced to seek additional land.

The logging trails built by timber contractors began to play a significant role at this point because they enabled new settlers to penetrate deeper and deeper into the forest. The dispersed patches cleared by Dayak farmers were now supplanted by broad agricultural frontiers.[35] Starting in 1985, 500,000 hectares of forest, an area approximately the size of the island of Bali, were annually converted to agriculture in Kalimantan alone.[36] Just as in Costa Rica, however, fires were not set solely for the purpose of alleviating hunger, but often for profit. Although the government laid claim to the forests, it had no means of protecting them. As a result, they became a virtual no-man's land. Truck-farmers living in towns now hire labourers to clear large areas where the best timber has already been skimmed off so they can plant marketable crops.[37] And the Buginese, a seafaring people who played an important role in the colonial spice trade, lay out extensive pepper plantations.[38]

The marginal soils on these islands are incapable of supporting such speculative forms of land use, however. Unless they can be restored under the protection of tree cover, these soils will be leached out, providing ideal conditions for invasion by *alang-alang*. In eastern Kalimantan alone, grassland spread so widely that it covered 400,000 hectares by 1980.[39]

Progress and Development?

Like other peoples, the Dayaks have been increasingly drawn into the market economy. Many groups have relocated downriver in recent decades in search of schools for their children, health care, and access to consumer goods and modern tools. Thus the chainsaw has come to replace the axe, and the paddle has been superseded by the outboard motor. Distances can now be covered in less time, and local markets are able to extend their reach deeper into the forest.

These developments have had diverse impacts on long-established modes of production. People who have traditionally processed rattan to make marketable products are careful not to exploit secondary forestland more than necessary, as the liana-like rattan palm needs trees to support it as it climbs.[40] Other groups living within range of a market tend to work larger patches of cleared land. Modern tools have made it easier to cut huge ironwood trees and split them into shingles.[41] Illipe trees – which are intended to benefit future generations, such as the *damar* trees in Krui – are now sold only for their timber, even if this

Box 7.1 Fire as a disastrous new site condition

In 1982 and 1983 there was no rain for months on end. The sun scorched the already damaged forest canopy and dried out the soil. Fires set to clear the land burned out of control along the lower course of the Mahakam River. Flames rapidly consumed the logging debris left on the forest floor and spread up the towering lianas to the treetops, where they ignited the crowns of the very tallest trees. The heat was so intense that even the thickest trees were blown to pieces by the force of exploding pockets of resin.

Fire ravaged the land for months until it was finally halted at the base of the mountains, which formed the boundary for timber concessions. Three and a half million hectares were either partly or totally destroyed in the largest forest fire that was ever recorded. Plumes of smoke drifted as far as Java and even interfered with air traffic in Singapore, 1500 kilometres away.[69] Although drought and small-scale fires had always occurred in the rainforest, forest fires were never before so extensive, so ferocious and so frequent. In 1987 and in 1991, there were major fires in Kalimantan, and in 1994 another five million hectares were affected in Sumatra and Kalimantan.[70]

Frequently recurring forest fires can be fatal to the rainforest. The first wave destroys parent trees, and the second regenerative growth, until a third or fourth fire finally has nothing left to consume but grassland.

obliterates the memory of the far-sighted individuals who originally planted them.[42]

'Progress' and 'development' were officially declared the motives of the reckless opening up of Kalimantan and Sumatra. But 30 to 40 million forest-dwellers, whose traditional rights were usurped by the state and granted to a few private

Brazil

The history of Amazonia is one of the exploitation of soil, vegetation and human beings – processes that have intensified in recent decades. In the 1960s Brazil's military rulers adopted policies that attracted large enterprises from the southern part of the country to Amazonia, where they operated generously subsidised cattle ranches and became a driving force behind land speculation. The military regime also enticed many landless people to the rainforest by building new roads and sponsoring settlement programmes. Despite these developments, it is not too late to save Amazonia. The region still has extensive areas of forest cover. Moreover, permanent settlement and use of the rainforest by non-Indian populations is also possible. This is reflected in the different 'tree cultures' practised by settlers of Japanese descent in Tomé Açu, by *caboclos* who live along river-banks and by rubber tappers.

Amazonia is a cultural landscape which has been cultivated and influenced by indigenous peoples for thousands of years. The small areas they cleared for cultivation were and are mere gaps in an endless sea of trees and pose no serious long-term threat to the forest. Vegetation reappears in the form of undisturbed primary forest after several decades (left), and only the trained eye can detect the traces of earlier Indian cultures, such as *pupunha* palms or groups of Brazil nut trees.

Large-scale burning of the forest to clear it for grazing is still considered a *benfeitoria*, or beneficial intervention. Cattle in Amazonia are particularly important as boundary markers for private property and as protection against expropriation (right). Land speculation, hoarding, parcelling and resale of land are much more profitable than beef production.

triggered a boom in development. More families emigrated from Japan. In 1957, as many as 800,000 pepper plants were vigorously climbing their supporting posts, while the price of pepper on the world market simultaneously continued its own rapid climb.[2] In 1961 the small Japanese community in Tomé Açu supplied more than 5 per cent of the world's pepper.

The 500 families in this community continued to live deep in the rainforest; the road from Tomé Açu to Belém was nothing more than a dirt path. Tomé Açu did build its own hospital, however, for the struggle against malaria became part of life here. The *Associaçao Cultural* provided a link between Tomé Açu and Japan, and served as an information centre as well as a centre of agricultural instruction and innovation. Ties with southern Brazil, where hundreds of thousands of Japanese had settled in the meantime, made it easier to conduct trade and obtain necessary working capital. Then suddenly, in the mid 1960s, pepper growers faced a crisis. The price of pepper on the world market collapsed at the same time that the leaves of the pepper plant were attacked by a fungus which inhibited growth.

Tree Gardens Take the Place of Monocultures

The treeless cultural landscape of Tomé Açu, which in the mid 1960s was still dominated by the orderly pattern of pepper plants, once again began to change. *Cecropia*, *Visma* and other pioneer species started to reestablish themselves on some abandoned pepper plantations, while others were converted to tree gardens.

Maki Takuro, who emigrated to Brazil in the period after the pepper boom, is one of a new breed of farmers who specialise in tree gardens, as evidenced by the wide variety of trees he cultivates. One of his gardens is a mixture of *macacauba*,[3] a source of valuable wood; *cupuaçu*, which produces the delectable fruit related to cacao that is very popular in Belém; and *açai*, a multipurpose palm whose stems can be cut to obtain *palmito*, an asparagus-like delicacy. However, Maki Takuro only cultivates and harvests what will fetch the best price at the moment. Should this happen to be *cupuaçu*, he fertilises the young *cupuaçu* trees with compost. If *palmito* is in demand, he cuts the *açai* so they will coppice. If there is little market for either of these, he concentrates on different products in his other tree gardens. Meanwhile, the

Brazil nut tree (para nut), a giant of the rainforest which produces thick, long nuts that make a tasty snack at any party.[15] This species, known locally as *castanha*, grows either in isolation or in groves that contain dozens of individual trees. It is a light-demanding gap opportunist which is thus found only in large clearings. It is likely that these trees germinated in groves on clearings where slash-and-burn agriculture had once been practised, and it is even possible that they were purposely planted by Amerindians. The Kayapó people still plant Brazil nut seeds today, along with other types of seeds.[16]

Though regarded by the industrialised world as a prehistoric, unspoiled landscape, Amazonia – in reality – developed and flourished as an ancient cultural landscape, much like the rainforests of Costa Rica or Kalimantan, shaped in part by the indigenous population who lived there. So-called 'untouched rainforests', which have long influenced our perception of primary forests, were largely an invention of the Romantic writers of the eighteenth century.[17]

The Contrasting Worlds of Rubber

In 1839 the American chemist Charles Goodyear invented the process of vulcanisation, in which raw rubber is heated with sulphur to make it stable. By the middle of the nineteenth century, telegraph lines insulated with rubber and the first rubber condoms were already on the market. Approximately 40 years later the Dunlop and Michelin companies began to manufacture bicycle and automobile tyres.[18] Rubber, available only from Amazonia at that time, had by then become an indispensable component of industrialisation, and demand skyrocketed.

Amazonian rubber was a product of starkly contrasting worlds. One was the *seringal* – the world of the rubber tapper, or *seringueiro*, which has changed little up to the present day. *Seringueiros* set out in the darkness of night along one of the paths that connect widely dispersed rubber trees, hanging pans on their trunks to catch the milky juice that drips from the places where they cut the bark. Later, they return to retrieve the latex that has collected in the pans, and spend the rest of the day heating it over a fire, which causes it to separate into layers and coagulate into elongated balls of latex.[19] At the end of the last century most *seringueiros* were natives of the *nordeste* who came from Ceará or other poor towns in the north-eastern part of Brazil. In times of economic crisis, thousands of *seringueiros* who were forced to migrate eventually made their way into even the most remote areas of the vast Amazon basin. While still in their native villages, they were recruited by a *seringalista*, who was the *de facto* owner of a *seringal*. The *seringalista* paid the travel costs of a future *seringueiro* and provided him with manioc flour, salt, coffee, ammunition, and fishhooks for his first rubber-tapping expedition, as well as enough *cachaça* for Sundays – all at exorbitant prices.[20]

Thus, before they even saw their first rubber tree, *seringueiros* had already assumed a heavy burden of debt from which they rarely succeeded in extricating themselves. From the time they started to work, they faced an ongoing struggle to pay off their growing debts with the rubber they produced. They were forbidden to cultivate their own manioc fields, as this could distract them from collecting latex. And if they tried to trade their rubber with anyone other than the *seringalistas* who sponsored them, they put their lives at risk.[21]

An altogether different world could be found in the cities of Manaus and Belém, with their trading houses and their direct links to New York and Liverpool. This was a world of extravagant wealth for those whose fortunes were based on the exploitation of rubber tappers and who existed as virtual serfs. The centre of Manaus was only three kilometres from the border of the dense rainforest. Yet despite its location and the stench of smouldering rubber which hung constantly in the air, making it smell like a glowing fire that had been doused with water, Manaus was one of the most elegant places on the face of the earth at the turn of the century. Thanks to the

Edgar Sassahara's *fazenda*.
Plantations of passion fruit and
other crops occupy only a
portion of the land, most of
which is covered with valuable
trees, tree gardens and other
agroforestry systems. The
fazenda also includes a large
patch of natural forest.

largest iron ore deposit was discovered at Carajás, in the southern part of the state of Pará. Meanwhile, tens of thousands of *garimpeiros* mined 14 tonnes of gold from the nearby Serra Pelada. This provided an even stronger incentive for those already active in business to stake claim to as much land as they could in the hope of being similarly blessed by good fortune. Moreover, money invested in land was money protected from the ravages of the terrible inflation then affecting the *cruzeiro*. Anyone 'improving' the forest could claim legal title to the land he worked. As in Costa Rica, evidence of such improvement, or *benfeitoria*, was a reflection of long-established European tradition; improvement was defined as the removal of trees, which were also perceived as an impediment to development. Moreover, the owners of improved land were entitled to claim additional forestland six times the size of the area they had cleared.[31]

In the end, the goal of large-scale ranching enterprises was not juicy cuts of beef but lavish subsidies and extensive land rights. In reality, the footprints of cattle in the red earth became nothing more than an imprint signifying ownership. Amazonian ranches are owned for speculative purposes rather than for production.

Amazonia Becomes an Escape Valve for the Landless

Huge *fazendas* and various large-scale projects such as the Carajá mines and the Tucuruí reservoir have not been the only influences on the course of development. Since the 1970s, landless settlers, who are the victims of agricultural modernisation both in fertile southern Brazil and in the *nordeste*, have increasingly played a role in deciding the fate of Amazonia.

Fertile land is extremely unevenly distributed in Brazil: more than 80 per cent of it is owned by approximately 5 per cent of the *latifundistas*. In 1985 35 million hectares lay fallow at a time when roughly ten million agricultural labourers possessed no land of their own.[32] Among other things, the aim of the military coup of 1964 was to prevent the carrying out of proposed land reforms which would have redistributed the holdings of the *latifundistas* to benefit landless small-scale farmers. Instead, the new regime provided generous subsidies to persuade *latifundistas* to modernise their operations and convert them to highly mechanised agribusiness enterprises. This had the effect of concentrating even more land in the hands of a few landowners.[33] In the fertile regions of central Brazil, for example, soybeans and oranges replaced coffee, which was vulnerable to frost. Coffee requires 83 days of manual labour per hectare as opposed to only three days for soybeans, thanks to mechanisation.[34] As a consequence, *latifundistas* increasingly dismissed the peasant labourers who had always been indispensable to farming. As they lost access to the land they had previously leased from large landowners, these peasants also lost the basis of their livelihood.

Depressed prices on the international soybean market, the result of speculation by North American companies, also forced farmers with small- and medium-scale operations to sell their land. These farmers were later to appear in Amazonia with relatively large amounts of money at their disposal.[35] In the *nordeste*, which was plagued by drought and had a feudal land-ownership structure, mechanised production of sugar cane was introduced. The government forced this move in the mid 1970s in order to obtain alcohol needed to produce gasohol. In this region, too, many families were forced to abandon land they had previously leased but did not own. The results were bread riots and violent conflicts over land.

The military regime sought to quell these disturbances by focusing on Amazonia as a place to resettle people who had been displaced from their traditional habitats. Land distribution began in 1970, a year of drought, when Brazil's president, Medici, promised the hungry, landless *nordestinos* 'a land without people for people without land.' He then opened the campaign to build the *Transamazônica*, a road stretching for 4900 kilometres through the rainforest. This route became the symbol of an extended network of new roads that grew to 45,000

A tree garden with *açai* palms and *cupuaçu*, a relative of cacao.

Thailand

Forest Villages: More Trees, Greater Prosperity

In the nineteenth century the King of Thailand guaranteed Britain open access to teak forests in the northern part of the country. Teak, an excellent wood for shipbuilding, was a pillar of the British Empire at the time. This concession helped to ensure that Thailand remained the only country in South-East Asia not to be colonised by a European power. Forest cover in Thailand has been drastically reduced in recent decades, even in areas where teak does not grow, and teak stands are now widely depleted. Following disastrous floods, the government decreed a nation-wide ban on timber felling in 1989. Forest villages such as Mae Moh continue to demonstrate that reforestation is possible. When Mae Moh was founded in the 1960s, forestry goals and social needs were given equal consideration. As a result, landless people have obtained the means to secure a livelihood, and teak trees have once again been planted extensively.

The men moved like ghosts through the morning mist, walking noiselessly on bare feet. Even though he was wearing boots, Reginald Campbell tried instinctively to tread as lightly as the coolies who preceded him. The sound of apes screeching in the treetops ahead mingled with the shrill squawking of a hornbill and the hollow echoes that resounded whenever dewdrops splashed against the large, egg-shaped leaves of the teak trees.

Campbell's lead coolie followed an exact course along the contour, taking constant care not to stray from the drainage divide. This was the only way to keep a sense of direction in these endless forests and have any hope of finding the way back again. Moreover, this was the only way to scan the dense forest landscape systematically in order to seek out each sturdy teak stem in the thick bamboo underbrush. The next tree, almost 50 metres high, with a thick, grooved stem, was given the number 742. With a few strokes of the axe, the coolies cut through its bark just above the roots, as they had done with the others. The 'belt' formed by this cutting action assured that the tree would die slowly and be dry enough when felled two years later to be floated downstream when the rivers rose during the monsoon season.

Teak Wallah

In 1920 Reginald Campbell arrived in the sweltering city of Bangkok, known as the 'Venice of the East' because of its many canals. The former British naval officer had signed on with an English company as a journeyman in the teak trade, or 'teak-wallah', as he referred to himself in a later account of his time in northern Thailand.[1]

Campbell's firm had secured extensive logging rights in northern Thailand, where conditions are optimal for teak trees to flourish. The Bombay Burmah Trading Corporation Ltd (BBTCL) employed hundreds of workmen to fell trees, and used 180 elephants to haul the stems to river-banks, while dozens of other workmen were responsible for the teak rafts floated downstream. The BBTCL even const-

ructed a 40-mile-long railway (64-kilometres long) in one area where teak was especially abundant.

Life in the teak jungle was difficult. Reginald Campbell lived with a minimum of comfort, sustaining himself on rice and chicken, tinned butter and coffee, which was filtered through an old sock by the coolie who worked as his cook. Conditions during the rainy season, complete with blood-sucking leeches which even crawled through the eyelets of his shoes, were hellish. Campbell placed tins of kerosene under the legs of his cot so that he could at least sleep peacefully without being bothered by termites. He was also forced to combat deadly cobras, loneliness and other demons that plagued his soul, malaria, and parasites that attacked the stomach and the gut. He endured these tropical tortures for five years – the same length of time it took for a BBTCL raft to make the 850-kilometre journey to Bangkok. At the end of this time he returned to England, to be replaced by another teak-wallah.

The Mythical Quality of Teak

Teak has been a treasured commodity since time immemorial. There was a steady flow of teak to China from present-day Thailand long before Europeans arrived. Japan imported teak from Java as early as the seventeenth century. It is even possible that the foundation of the Tower of Babel was made of this durable wood, which is resistant to rot as well as insects: excavations of Babylonian temples have uncovered teak which probably came from the west coast of India.

In the late eighteenth century the British became the first Europeans to show an interest in teak. By that time, Britain's legendary oak forests had already been greatly depleted in order to supply wood needed to construct ships for the Royal Navy. Oak suitable for ship construction was of enormous strategic value to the British Empire, and it was becoming increasingly difficult to find, not only in Britain but on the European Continent as well. The west coast of India, however, was covered with abundant

Previous page: A *bunma paido* ('happy, toothless bull elephant') approaching a teak stem which he will drag out of the forest. Teak smugglers also favour these silent and amazingly agile work animals.

A Karen farmer with his grandchild (left); a Karen settlement in the hills of northern Thailand (above).

forests of teak, which was a perfect substitute for oak. In 1805 the 36-cannon frigate *Salsette*, the first battleship constructed completely of teak, was launched in Bombay. Between 1830 and 1855, skilled Indian shipbuilders working under British direction constructed a total of 123 large ships made of teak.

The British appetite for teak soon became insatiable. The construction of every ship consumed thousands of stems, and enormous quantities of high-quality timber were also sent to England for other purposes. Around 1850, the demands of the Empire forced the British to turn to the forests of Burma as well. Access to teak was ensured by three wars with Burma, the last of which openly revolved around the fortunes of Reginald Campbell's future employer, whose interests had been threatened by French intrigue at the court of the King of Burma.[2]

The Politics of Teak

History took a different course in Siam, which has been known as Thailand since 1939.

Although Thailand – 'land of the free' – was the only country in South-East Asia not to be colonised, Europeans none the less had a major influence there, the British foremost among them. The Chiang Mai treaties of 1874 and 1883, which forced Siam to guarantee European access to teak, were signed as a result of British pressure.[3]

Teak grows primarily in the northern part of Thailand, in the provinces of Chiang Mai, Lampang, Phrae and Nan. The monsoon climate in this region, combined with a dry season lasting for several months, is ideal for the teak tree, as is the soil. Teak is also partly resistant to the forest fires that occur during the dry months, a fact which further strengthened its dominance in the region.

Two ethnic groups live in northern Thailand: the Thai, who are Buddhists and grow rice in flooded fields on the plains, and tribes such as the Karen, shifting cultivators who live in the hills. Their agro-economic system is known as *taungya*, meaning 'field crops of the hills'. As early as the middle of the last

The People's Republic of China

Millions Help to Plant the Green Great Wall

Since 1949 the people of China have planted billions of trees over more than 30 million hectares. The most ambitious of several large-scale tree-planting efforts is the Green Great Wall, a system of protective forests designed to check the impacts of wind and airborne sand throughout northern China. The long struggle against the ravages of wind erosion is exemplified by the village of Hu Zhai, located 240 kilometres west of Beijing in the province of Shanxi, at the edge of the desert-like steppes of inner Mongolia. As recently as a few decades ago, Hu Zhai was at risk of being literally blown away. Today, with support from a Chinese–German forestry project known as 'Jinshatan', the residents of Hu Zhai are busy installing a second generation of windbreaks.

The village of Hu Zhai has long been at the mercy of tyrannical forces emanating from Mongolia. Although it is now centuries since the last bloody battles were fought along the Great Wall of China, which branches northwards and southwards not far from Hu Zhai, the struggle against Mongolian forces is not over. Every spring, far to the north, cold air masses begin a turbulent journey from Siberia to inner Mongolia, where they gather the strength which propels them across northern China. Here, they absorb immeasurable quantities of dust and sand before sweeping as far south as Beijing and even beyond.

In Hu Zhai, which is close to the industrial town of Datong, these weather conditions were responsible for a continual series of disasters until the 1960s. 'The seeds we sowed in the morning', says commune president Ning Kai, 'were often swept away by evening. The windstorms even unearthed freshly planted potatoes.' Airborne sand chapped and reddened the faces of field labourers and constantly gritted between their teeth. People who stayed in their homes when the winds came were careful to keep a shovel handy so they could dig themselves out after the storm had subsided. Metres of sand piled up against houses, some of which collapsed under the weight, and dunes began to form along the northern border of the village. As the desert advanced, the villagers retreated; by the 1950s, all but eight families had fled Hu Zhai.

Trees Fall Victim to the Ravages of War

In the village of Hu Zhai, and throughout extensive areas of northern China, where the fertile plains were permanently settled several millennia before settlement took place in Europe, environmental degradation has resulted primarily from the destruction of natural forests over the course of many thousands of years. A number of Chinese overlords expressed concern about forests and sustainable use of forest resources as early as several centuries before the birth of Christ, indicating that trees may already have become scarce in some areas

by that time. During the Zhou Dynasty (1100–221 BC) people who failed to plant a sapling on the spot where they had felled a tree were not granted wood for their coffins.[1] After one heavy storm the Emperor Chen even commanded his vassals to raise every tree that had been blown over.[2]

Timber was needed for every edifice, whether it was a private dwelling, a temple or a palace. The construction of palaces and administrative buildings required enormous amounts of wood, especially since these structures often had to be rebuilt after they were destroyed by fire during popular insurrections. Such was the fate of the Chin Dynasty palace, which was so vast that it is said to have burned for three whole months.[3] Construction and subsequent additions to the Imperial Palace in Beijing, which was destroyed by fire at the beginning of the Ming Dynasty (1368–1644), continued for centuries; as time went by, timber had to be obtained from forests at increasingly distant locations.[4]

The felling of trees paved the way for settlement in China, just as it does today in the rainforests of Indonesia and other countries. As early as the fourth century BC, the Chinese philosopher Mencius noted that after trees were felled in the Niu Mountains, there were still enough seedlings and coppices to ensure that the forest would regenerate. But because goats and other animals continually browsed on this new growth until nothing was left, the mountains were eventually denuded. No one who subsequently viewed these clear-cut areas would have imagined that a dense forest once flourished there.[5] Continual warfare also took a toll on the forests of northern China. Forests were set on fire as a strategic move to smoke out the enemy, and wherever overlords rode, their paths first had to be cleared within bowshot in order to protect them from assassins.[6]

By the nineteenth century, trees had become so scarce in China that timber needed for maintenance of the Imperial Palace in Beijing and for construction of the Quing tombs had to be imported from Oregon.[7] The shortage of wood even had a deep influence on Chinese

Previous page: The Green Great Wall: a modern system of protection in a traditional setting.

China was once subject to constant invasions by Mongolian tribes (above). As a result of the deforestation that occurred then, the country now suffers from the ravages of Mongolian storms (right).

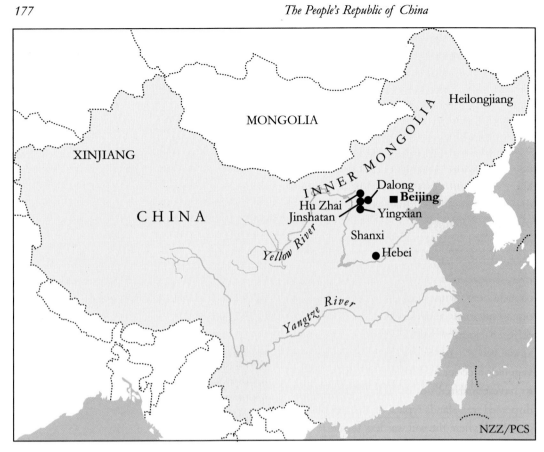

The Tree Monsters of Los Angeles

Is there any point in planting trees in a city like Los Angeles? A group known as TreePeople is convinced that the answer is 'yes', and they have ample proof to back up their conviction. For almost a quarter of a century, TreePeople, a non-profit, non-governmental organization, has pursued three main objectives: reforestation of smog-damaged forests in the hills surrounding Los Angeles; planting trees in the city itself; and environmental education, which is aimed primarily at children. Many of the 1.5 million saplings planted directly by Tree-People, or as a result of one of their campaigns, have since grown to maturity. And many of the approximately one million young people from the streets of Los Angeles who have experienced the feel of earth and seedlings in their hands, thanks to TreePeople, have since grown up to become environmentally literate citizens prepared to assume civic responsibility.

The children crowded excitedly around the mysterious door behind which they imagined the tree monster was hiding. A nearby poster displayed the questions: 'Who has the power to plant trees? Who can start an entire forest? Who can make drastic improvements in the environment?' The answer printed beneath the questions read: 'The tree monster! Only the tree monster!' As the children at the rear drew further back, one courageous girl stepped forward to open the door – and found herself staring at her own image in a mirror.

You are the tree monster; *you* are the one who can make a difference; *you* can do something; *you* can change the world. This is the central message of TreePeople, a non-profit, non-governmental organization headquartered in Coldwater Canyon Park, in the hills above the exclusive suburb of Beverly Hills. I first heard of TreePeople in a strangely roundabout way, when Suderlal Bahuguna told me about the group during my visit to his ashram deep in the Himalayas (see Chapter 2).

School classes and groups of children accompanied by their parents visit Coldwater Canyon Park almost daily in order to learn something about trees. Here they can discover the holly, the bush from which the nearby movie capital took its name. Or they can see the notorious poison oak, whose leaves cause outbreaks of rash and itching as soon as they come in contact with the skin of Caucasians. Native Americans, however, who are immune to this reaction, found many uses for the poison oak. Among other things, they took it as an antidote to the poison of rattlesnake bites.[1] Older children learn how tree canopies provide cool shade in the asphalt jungles of Los Angeles, and how walls and façades can 'disappear' behind shrubs and climbing plants. In addition to having a cooling effect on urban heat islands, trees and other plants also reduce the city's contribution to the greenhouse effect.

On visits to Coldwater Canyon Park, parents and teachers engage in intense discussions about the positive aspects of trees. Although they are based on verifiable observations, the benefits of trees are difficult to quantify. One example is a study done in the state of Delaware, which showed that convalescing patients recover more quickly and are less likely to suffer from depression if they can see natural foliage from their hospital beds.[2] Then there is the case of Edison Middle School in South Central Los Angeles, whose dismal appearance could easily cause it to be mistaken for a prison. The school principal at Edison noticed a decline in student violence and an improvement in performance following a tree-planting campaign.[3] Or there is the example of the New York City policemen who joined children in planting trees in Harlem and the Bronx, with the result that relations between the local population and the police improved notably, and the crime rate in both neighbourhoods declined markedly.[4]

TreePeople believe that the exposure to trees which children and adolescents get at Coldwater Canyon Park is one step along the way to becoming environmentally literate citizens. But this educational programme, which now reaches about 100,000 young people annually, is not the only activity in which TreePeople is engaged. The group is also committed to reforestation of the hills around Los Angeles, and it was the first non-profit organisation to practice urban forestry. By the mid 1990s, TreePeople had either inspired or been directly involved in the planting of over 1.5 million trees.

Previous page:
Do giant sequoia trees grow from the seeds of small cones or large ones?

Scenes from a visit by a group of
children to Coldwater Canyon
Park: a holly bush (left);
experiencing the feel of earth in
one's hands and planting the seed
of a tree (above).

The group of volunteer planters.

Andy Lipkis with actor Gregory Peck, who serves on the board of directors of TreePeople.

'A day like this makes you feel good'. Volunteer Paul Axinn's hands after planting day.

The Million-Tree Campaign

In 1980 the City of Los Angeles Planning Department released the findings of a study on trees and air quality. The study found that an additional one million trees, once they had grown to maturity, would filter great quantities of particulate dust from the air and noticeably improve living conditions in the city. But city crews working alone would need 20 years to plant the trees, and an additional 400 million US dollars would have to be raised through taxes to pay for planting and subsequent maintenance.

Tom Bradley, the mayor of Los Angeles at the time, appealed to TreePeople. The organisation had won public trust and respect by mobilising thousands of volunteers during the recent flood crisis, and by helping out in other situations where the authorities were too over-burdened to cope. These successful ventures had confirmed the group's faith in its own idealism. With renewed confidence, Tree-People launched a campaign in July 1981 to plant one million trees in the three years leading up to the Los Angeles Summer Olympics of 1984.

One million trees! In Europe, the very mention of this figure would be enough to discourage the most eager enthusiast. 'The figure had a good solid ring about it,' says Andy Lipkis, 'one that we felt could inspire great volunteer efforts within the community.' And so TreePeople set out to achieve its 'impossible' three-year goal. Three turbulent years ensued. The overall game plan was clear, but there were no set rules. TreePeople found itself constantly searching for new ways to popularise the vision of planting one million trees and to inspire the public's imagination.

The proximity of Hollywood suggested the movie capital as an obvious source of potential aid. After dozens of attempts had been made to enlist the help of Hollywood personalities in publicising the campaign, the actor Gregory Peck finally agreed to film a television spot. Peck eventually found himself so convinced by the cause that he became a member of TreePeople's board of directors. Efforts to get support from billboard companies were less successful. Billboard producers are likely to see trees as their 'natural enemies' because they block the messages posted on boards. TreePeople later learned that one of the companies it approached had actually been prosecuted for carrying out a midnight massacre of trees.

In addition to engaging in the public relations work necessary for this campaign, the staff of TreePeople, numbering less than a dozen men and women, found themselves hurrying from one activity to another, supported by citizen foresters and some 200 sympathetic activists. City police helped with planting in the Hispanic neighbourhoods of East Los Angeles. For three consecutive years the police and other authorities even blocked traffic for one day on portions of the Marino Freeway so that 5000 volunteers could use it to hold a ten kilometre run and plant trees along its borders.

An Olympic Effort Succeeds

At one point in the campaign TreePeople faced the task of transporting 100,000 seedlings donated by a nursery that was going out of business. The national guard was persuaded to help out by providing a convoy of large trucks,

Forest Farming in the Black Forest: an Existence Based on Trees

Timber has been exported from the heart of Germany's Black Forest for hundreds of years. Today many farmers who own large private tracts of forestland still earn their livelihood from timber production. Despite this economic exploitation of a natural resource – or perhaps because of it – the forests have remained intact. Some forest farmers have even been able to preserve traditional ways of using forest resources, but only by strongly resisting prevailing trends in forest sciences and government bureaucracy. These farmers forgo clear-cutting in order to harvest trees selectively, thereby ensuring the survival of mixed forests where different species can grow side-by-side, from seedlings to mature trees. Johannes Gross, a forest farmer who lives in the village of Oberwolfach, manages his forestland in this way, attempting to augment traditional methods with state-of-the-art knowledge. Resource use of this sort illustrates how many forests in Germany could be transformed into biotic communities, where forest management is based on natural processes taking their course with a minimum of human intervention.

Johannes Gross and Walter Schmidtke determine the direction in which the tree is to be felled.

Sawing away
At the branches on which they were sitting,
They noisily exchanged information
About how to saw more efficiently
Before plummeting to the ground with a great
*　crash.*
Those who witnessed this merely shook their
*　heads*
And energetically continued their sawing.

　　　　　　　　　　　　- Bertolt Brecht

Johannes Gross had begun to saw at a point high up in the tree. Leaving the last third of the crown untouched, he slowly worked his way downwards, completely lopping off one branch after another as he went. When the last branch had fallen, he embraced the tree with both arms, and slid deftly down the remaining two meters of the smooth stem. He then selected the next promising spruce tree, placed his ladder against it, and proceeded to wind his way upwards through the branches to begin the process of pruning once again.

Gross is certainly not one to saw off the branch that supports him. Both he and Walter Schmidtke, the forester who advises him, believe that he will reap future rewards from the labour he performs on his trees. When they are ripe for harvesting in approximately 100 years, his trees, now between 15 and 35 years old, will produce valuable, high-quality timber which is free of branch holes. Lopping off the branches also allows more light to strike the forest floor, where it helps to nurture fir and beech seedlings, enriching the mixture of species in the forest.

Johannes Gross is the owner of a farm called Thesenhof. Walter Schmidtke, a retired forester who used to work with Gross's father, still pays regular visits to Thesenhof, located in the commune of Oberwolfach, deep in the narrow valley of the Gelbach, a small stream which flows into the Wolf River. The Wolf later joins the Kinzig, a tributary of the Rhine, in Wolfach. The main house at Thesenhof is an imposing, well-groomed structure, like many

Previous page:
The Black Forest as seen from Brandenkopf, near Oberwolfach.

other farmhouses on the widely dispersed farms in this region. The meadows surrounding it are so steep that the cows which graze on them cannot recline to digest their feed, so they must be driven back to their stalls at midday. This green landscape is interrupted only by small potato patches, which rapidly dissolve into the seemingly endless tree stands typical of the Black Forest region today.

Farmers and Freemen

In trying to understand why Johannes Gross is willing to climb high into the branches of his trees to perform labour from which he himself will receive no direct benefit, it is important to understand that he considers himself the present-day representative of a long line of forest farmers. He oversees Thesenhof as a perpetual trust inherited from his ancestors, which he will one day pass onto his own heirs. Thesenhof is a very old farm indeed. Although

the year 1571 is engraved in a stone on one of its walls, the house undoubtedly existed prior to that date. The Kinzig and the Wolf valleys were settled between the eleventh and the thirteenth centuries by the Alemanni, a Germanic tribe. At that time the floors of both valleys consisted mostly of swampland and were not yet habitable, and the side valleys and the hills were as rugged and steep as they are today. Clearing the mighty fir, beech and spruce from this landscape must have been a task of almost superhuman proportions. Only large farms with a labour force sufficient to do all the necessary work could hope to survive in such an environment. Anyone willing to settle here received a grant of personal freedom from the Counts of Fürstenberg – a special incentive at a time when many people in this part of southern Germany were still serfs whose fate was largely in the hands of their masters.

As landlords, however, the Counts of Fürstenberg retained legal ownership of the land; even freemen were obliged to pay a tribute consisting of a certain number of chickens each year, in addition to other duties. The Fürstenbergs also laid claim to a third of the value of a farm when it was passed on to an heir. To ensure that this tax was applied as infrequently as possible, the youngest son was usually designated as the sole heir to the family property. This practice also prevented the break-up of a family's holdings, helping to maintain the minimum size necessary for a farm to subsist. Children who left home received a modest bequest; afterwards they hired themselves out as day labourers on other farms, worked as labourers processing forest products, or moved down-river to the cities.[1] Young women would hope to marry and settle on another farm. Men also married and settled elsewhere, however, as some farms had only female heirs, like Johannes Gross's great-grandfather. When he took up residence at Thesenhof in 1900 at the age of 34, ten or more people were living and working on the farm, which was entirely self-sufficient in food production.

During this time, land in the heart of the Black Forest was clear-cut to cultivate the which illustrates how timber became an increasingly important source of revenue for local sovereigns in the eighteenth century. In the final analysis, the economic value of timber was probably responsible for the birth of forestry as a modern discipline. And it was certainly just as important as the struggle against the centuries-old ghost of timber shortages, which various rulers never hesitated to conjure up when they felt it necessary to promote their own interests in timber or wild game at the expense of their subjects.[10] Modern scientific forestry was first developed in Prussia and Saxony in the mid eighteenth century, and subsequently spread widely in a form that came to be recognised as classic German forestry. The central task of this new discipline was to produce as much timber as possible in the most rational way. Traditional methods of pacing off the forest and making rough assessments of timber stands were now replaced by exact standards of measurement and careful planning. The so-called 'standard tree' was introduced in calculations carried out in forestry offices, where it took the place of the actual living tree for the purpose of simulating forest development and projecting future timber harvests and expected revenues.

Outdoors, meanwhile, forestry engineers began to survey traditional mixed forests, dividing them up like a chessboard. Where trees were expected to grow for 100 years, 100 growing plots were planned. Each year one plot would be clear-cut and subsequently reforested, usually with a single species. The aim was to produce stands in which trees of the same age and the same species would grow together. The inclination of early foresters to promote monocultures was based to some extent on the good experience they had with spruce and pine, which grew rapidly not only on overgrazed sites but also in areas frequently characterised as completely degraded patches of forestland.

Given the perspective of their time, it is perhaps easier to understand why foresters in the eighteenth century were initially so consumed by the quantifying spirit of the times.

From our present perspective, however, chessboard forestry – large-scale clear-cutting and planting of monocultures by age classes – has had both regrettable impacts in Germany and far-reaching effects on forestry practices worldwide.

Selective versus Large-Scale Harvesting

Chessboard forestry techniques, which were fashioned to meet the challenges of growing trade and capital investment, also penetrated the heart of the Black Forest. By 1833 scientific forestry was acknowledged in the forestry law of Baden, which summarily forbade the selective felling of trees – a practice described in the law as an inefficient and uneconomical method that violated all the rules of forestry.[11] Even the traditional single-tree selection system of the Kinzig and Wolf valleys was now to be replaced by chessboard forestry, with planting used as a regeneration technique. Farmers in the region reacted vehemently against such authoritarian attempts to direct their activities. Numerous communes protested by repeatedly petitioning the government, and tempers flared to the extent that forestry officials became the targets of violence.[12]

The situation only began to improve four decades later when Joseph Schätzle, the son of a Black Forest carpenter, became the district forester in Wolfach. Schätzle, who seems to have comprehended that selective cutting was a sensible approach to forestry, refused to acknowledge the legal ban on the *Plenterwald* system. Speaking to a gathering of the Baden forestry association in 1884, he maintained that the single-tree selection system was the closest thing to original, natural forests. Eventually, stiff opposition from farmers, combined with the passive resistance of its own officials, influenced the forestry administration of Baden. Before the turn of the century, the ban on *Plenterwald* was modified and selective harvesting of trees was tolerated.

The 'Grosse Tannen' reserve near Kälberbronn, an original forest, is a mosaic of trees of different species and sizes. Particularly noticeable are the many beech trees among towering firs and the small percentage of spruce.

Nature Retaliates against an Emphasis on Quantity over Quality

In the latter part of the nineteenth century, the qualitative disadvantages of chessboard forestry were made obvious again and again by the ravages of storms, snow and pests, severely shaking the faith of many foresters in approaches based on the extreme manipulation of natural forests. By 1880, Karl Gayer, a professor of silviculture in Munich, urged that nature be taken as a model. He warned that foresters must mend the error of their ways by adopting a course that would return them to the *Plenterwald* system. This was the opening salvo in a long-running debate about whether trees should be harvested selectively or cultivated on plots. This debate, which has continued to the present day, was initially characterised by sharp verbal exchanges and raw emotion. Those who advocated chessboard forestry were blamed for its failure to maintain fir trees in mountain forests. They struck back by charging that the

Plenterwald system was little more than a 'spiritual exercise', a 'myth' and an expression of 'barbaric backwoods culture'.[13]

Many related topics of concern were already being debated in the nineteenth century. The proponents of *Plenterwald* argued that man cannot decree what and how much nature should produce over the course of a century.[14] Nor can the forest simply be regarded as a timber factory. Sustainable use of forest resources must be based on quality as well as quantity; planned forests with trees in specific age classes will be forests of substandard quality. A high-quality forest, by contrast, is a near-natural biotic community that is cushioned against potentially negative external interference and can rapidly recover, remaining largely self-regulating and stable over the long term.

Plenterwald exhibits these very features to a high degree. Like other forests, for example, it has permanent populations of bark beetles. But while they have caused widespread deterioration in spruce monocultures, bark beetles have

The reasons for stagnating timber revenues are the same in Germany as in Switzerland: because declining energy prices have reduced transport costs, timber that is exploited cheaply in the tropics, Canada and Eastern Europe has now penetrated Central European markets. This also applies to timber imported from Scandinavia, where costs are reduced by large-scale, fully mechanised logging operations. Wood has also faced stiff competition from other materials. The steel industry has been subsidised for decades in an attempt to preserve jobs, and the inexpensive energy used to process both steel and concrete constitutes a form of indirect subsidies. Meanwhile, ecological benefits, such as the favourable energy balance that would result from the use of wood, remain hidden.

Natural Regeneration, Adequate Infrastructure and Low Production Costs

Most public and many private forest owners in Baden–Württemberg suffered heavy losses during the winter storms of 1990 and have recovered only slowly due to sluggish demand, low prices and high operating costs. The effects of this poor economic climate have also been felt at Thesenhof, although conditions there produced an initially stabilising effect on farm operations. Valuable timber – wood with desirable dimensions that will bring a good price – is now in good supply in carefully managed forests. Logging trails to transport timber were largely completed in the 1980s, when economic conditions were better. A good network of logging trails is necessary for environmentally sound maintenance of *Plenterwald* systems, which require light but regular selective harvesting.

While regeneration in chessboard forests is usually done by planting – which can cost as much as 10,000 Deutschmarks per hectare, depending on the species – nature does most of the work free of charge in the forests of Thesenhof. Private hunting rights also allow

Johannes Gross to control the wildlife population in order to maintain a balance between wildlife and trees, which is favourable to regeneration.

There are virtually no external labour costs at Thesenhof. Johannes Gross normally performs most of the labour himself or with the help of his son Hubertus, who will one day take over the farm. It can be hazardous to work alone in the forest, although Gross himself has been lucky so far. He suffered an injury only once, when he cut his knee with a chainsaw and was hospitalised for 14 days. Monotonous labour sometimes strains his back, and the pain robs him of several hours of sleep at night. His successors, however, will presumably have an easier time of it. The more closely the forests at Thesenhof approximate the balanced conditions typical of *Plenterwald*, the less labour will be involved in harvesting, regeneration and maintenance.

Johannes Gross removes branches from one of his trees (left). A stand showing the first signs of trees at different stages of development (right). Beech, an important species, is still lacking. Restoring near-natural forests is particularly difficult wherever there are uniform monocultures of spruce where indigenous species are no longer present, or where young trees are destroyed by herds of wild game.

Plenterwald is a cultural product. It is a 'family forest' where, thanks to adept harvesting, fir, spruce and various deciduous trees grow in an intimate mixture of seedlings and full mature seeds.

Increasing Market Share with Sustainably Produced Timber

If the market for timber continues to deteriorate, however, the economic foundations of forest management created at Thesenhof will also be undermined, with the result that decades of effort and labour may well be lost.

This is even more likely where the transition is only now being made from chessboard forests to multistructured forests characterised by a mixture of species. Mixed forests will certainly regenerate as the result of natural processes, but this will take centuries. In most places natural development will be hastened by a combination of timber use and planting of species appropriate to the site, in order to produce forests of satisfactory quality. At many sites, however, taking no action at all is likely to produce greater improvements than an overly activist approach.

If we are ever to make a serious commitment to sustainability of the sort that has been discussed and debated since the 1992 Earth Summit in Rio de Janeiro, we will not be able to ignore the world's forests: timber is bound to play a key role in any such commit-ment.

Raising the price of energy to reflect ecological costs is the most important step that can be taken at present. This will gradually highlight the advantages of timber – a renew-able resource which can be produced sustainably with positive impacts on the envir-onment. However, imposing energy taxes is a slow and difficult step to take. Meanwhile, a few global environmental organisations, such as the Worldwide Fund for Nature and Greenpeace, are taking a different approach. They advocate a system of certification, which will allow customers to recognise and purchase wood products which are made from timber grown in sustainably managed forests. The foremost objective of certification is to reduce the ruthless exploitation now taking place in some of the world's forests. This approach would also make high-quality indigenous timber more economically competitive.

Efforts are also underway to make wood more attractive in the construction industry, which represents the largest single market for timber. Until recently, wood was a resource fashioned primarily by hand, through the acquired skills of a carpenter. Moreover, it is still hampered by a historical form of prejudice rooted in the fires that plagued cities in medieval times. Nevertheless, wood has now become a dependable modern construction material with good potential, thanks to innovative developments such as gluing techniques. The next step is to eliminate obstacles on the drawing-board. Engineers and architects already know how to work with steel and concrete, but tools to help them plan structures made of wood are only just being developed – especially since research and training institutions have neglected this aspect of construction technology.[22]

Sometimes surprising market-driven solutions appear. Fir, for example, has long suffered from competitive disadvantages because demand for spruce was on the rise. Fir trees with the dimensions of the classic 'Dutch fir' have faced particular hurdles, as today very few sawmills have the equipment needed to process them. Since 1994, however, tens of thousands of cubic metres of fir have been exported annually to Japan. The Japanese timber industry is currently facing a shortage of supply, since sturdy tropical timber has become increasingly difficult to obtain. In recent years Japan has also imported less timber from the United States, where restrictions have been imposed on large-scale logging operations in certain old growth forests in order to protect endangered animal species. The path taken by timber from the Black Forest to the Pacific has long been familiar, however. Today, this timber is transported on freighters down the Rhine from Kehl to Rotterdam, and then across the Pacific to Japan on the same ships used to import automobiles destined for sale in Europe.[23]

Making Dangerous Tools Harmless

Policy-makers, on the other hand, are not likely to provide any surprise solutions such as subsidies. While forest owners such as Johannes Gross fulfil their social and ecological obligations to a high degree, public policy takes little account of either forests or forest farmers. The state of Baden–Württemberg is an exception, however. Since 1991, owners of private forestland have benefited from a compensatory payment which can be as high as 120 Deutschmarks per hectare.

Payments of this sort still do not compensate for the many public benefits the forest provides, such as recreation and its role in soil and water conservation, and they certainly do nothing to compensate for environmental stress linked to new forms of forest degradation. Restructuring the existing market economy in accordance with ecological principles would be a much fairer and economically more efficient approach than the use of subsidies. It is the market economy in its current form which entices us, as consumers, to apply sharp saws to the branches that support us.

Conclusion : Forests of Hope?

Whether in Saklana in the Himalayas, Machame on Mount Kilimanjaro, or Tomé Açu in Amazonia, the fate of trees and forests is determined by human needs and human interests. In the final analysis, political and economic power, conditions of ownership and questions of dependency and empowerment are the decisive issues. While tree species and plant communities vary throughout the world, all human societies are characterised by conflicts involving the short-sightedness of individuals versus the long-term needs of the community; the desire for quick profit versus sustainable returns; and economic activity versus ecological responsibility. The concluding remarks presented here constitute an attempt to outline the combined effects of these forces on trees and forests, giving particular attention to const-ructive forces which offer reason for hope.

The Struggle to Promote Sustainable Resource Use

In villages that exist at subsistence level, far removed from cities and with virtually no commercial ties to the outside world, forests fulfil many needs. They supply energy, food, fodder, fertiliser and medicine, as well as a wide range of raw materials. This situation existed in the industrialised world 150 years ago – a mere generation in the life of a tree – in places where urban centres now thrive at a feverish pace. And it still exists today in areas at the margins of settlement in the North as well as in the tropics.

The term 'village' has an idyllic ring, suggesting a sense of community that ensures survival, provides care in old age, and offers a setting where natural death occurs under normal conditions. But village life is also characterised by modest living conditions, physical labour, rigid gender roles, and social stratification, all of which imply conflict – over trees and forest products, among other things. Most controversies at the village level involve overexploitation of natural resources.

Village-dwellers, who are not free to abandon their remote settlements at will, are continually confronted with the need to negotiate rules for use of their natural resources. Although people in powerful positions attempt to gain even more in the process of such negotiations, underprivileged groups are still able to subsist by occupying social niches.

Resource use at the village level, which is frequently extensive, gives rise to cultural landscapes characterised by long-term stability, where regeneration occurs rapidly in the wake of degradation. There may be changes in the flora and fauna in such landscapes, but the broad range of indigenous species is preserved over time. Moreover, human-induced processes of selection and breeding lead to the development of new species, even in the forest. Human use of trees and forests has also produced many biological niches for flora and fauna that have special needs. Even in Amaz-onia, present-day biological diversity would not be as rich as it is without the presence of human beings.[1]

Rural–Urban Conflicts and the Depletion of Forest Resources

Many villages long ago came under the influence of cities where population and power are concentrated. Cities function as 'black holes' which devour both energy and resources. In order to ensure a supply of timber for use as a raw material and as a source of energy, cities were quick to claim official rights of resource use, even in remote forests. Forest services in Europe were founded to protect these rights. Early foresters, who were the first experts on energy and natural resources, served chiefly as representatives of urban economic interests.

Thus it was that in addition to rural conflicts over resource use, conflicts also arose between rural people and city-dwellers – in other words, between a world dominated by subsistence agriculture and one dominated by a market economy. Because subsistence farmers regard forests and fields as an integrated whole and establish no artificial boundaries between them, their traditional practices are a continual thorn in the side of foresters. They allow livestock to browse freely, hindering the growth of timber earmarked for urban needs, and cut branches to obtain leaf fodder, stunting the growth of trees and deforming them. The rural–urban conflict over resource use was clearly reflected in the early terminology used by foresters, who referred to timber produced for urban needs as a 'primary forest product', while rural needs were met by 'minor forest products'.

In order to ensure that their interests prevailed, powerful cities fashioned a silvicultural world of their own and attempted to keep local people from intruding in it. Foresters functioned primarily as policemen who restricted, forbade or even summarily expropriated traditional village rights of resource use. It is precisely such forms of intervention at the local level, however, which have provoked indigenous peoples everywhere to engage in activities that slowly but surely destroy the forests.

Every step taken by foresters against the will of local people is doomed to failure sooner or later. Commenting on the situation in the Bernese Oberland in 1818, district forester Karl Kasthofer predicted that forestry regulations would do as little to preserve Alpine forests as moral codes did to improve moral conduct. This realisation was an important reason for the eventual division of forest ownership in the Oberland among the state, among the village-level communities and among private interests. The example of the Bernese Oberland shows how difficult it is to privatise public forestland if social justice is denied. When rural elites try to take advantage of new regulations to promote their own interests, the underprivileged lose their customary rights and the social niches which they have traditionally occupied.

Large-Scale Resource Use Leads to Overexploitation

Overexploitation of resources did, indeed, occur in many parts of Central Europe in the early nineteenth century, hand-in-hand with rapid economic development. The demand for timber, accompanied by a rise in timber prices, meant that mature trees were felled with increasing regularity. While people in rural areas had previously cut trees selectively to meet specific needs, clear-cutting was now taking place on a large scale. Regeneration was hindered, however, because the underprivileged classes allowed their animals to browse more freely than ever and to trespass across newly established boundaries which they found unacceptable.

As long as 150 years ago some foresters began to question the extent to which the desire for profit could be allowed free rein before it posed a threat to the ecological function of forests. They also began to express concerns about protecting the work of previous generations – which represented both hope and security for the future – from the whims of a particular generation.[2] Nineteenth-century forestry laws were partly influenced by these ethical considerations; even today, the miracle of reforestation in Central Europe is often attributed to these laws. But with the benefit of hindsight, it now seems clear that the return of the trees was much more likely a result of the thoroughgoing social and economic changes that took place in the mid nineteenth century.

Large-scale use of coal, the 'subterranean forest', was a decisive development. Coal reduced the urban demand for timber as a source of energy and promoted industrial-isation. This was the first step in the great transformation of Karl Kasthofer's society, characterised by traditional, biologically based solar energy, to the modern mass consumer society we know today. Many people began to move from rural areas to cities, where they took jobs in newly established factories.

Ancient conflicts over resource use disappeared in the whirlwind of development that took place in the age of coal. As pressure on the forests was reduced, it was finally possible to separate agriculture from forestry, and the long-heralded vision of forestry as an independent discipline moved closer to becoming reality. Gradually, foresters assumed the role of advisers rather than policemen.

From Woodlands to Monocultures and Back

The transformation of timber from an item of everyday use to a commercial commodity fundamentally changed the character of Central European forests. This was especially true where chessboard forestry replaced forests which had been used in traditional ways, and in which regeneration had occurred naturally. In many places this produced uniform coniferous forests where there had once been mixed deciduous forests.

Heated debates had already begun to rage among foresters prior to 1870. Those who favoured a natural approach argued that concentrating exclusively on timber production was an unnatural form of forest use for which a price would eventually have to be paid in terms of poor yields. Counter-arguments were advanced by advocates of modern forestry techniques, who scoffed at the 'pompous words' associated with natural forest management. At the same time, the arguments then being advanced for the orderly planting of trees were also early evidence of a primitive fear that is still widespread among foresters today: if nature can take care of forests without human intervention – through natural regeneration – there is no need for foresters. Furthermore, recurring catastrophes in the forests of Central Europe convincingly demonstrated that only species appropriate to a particular site can resist the ravages of storms and pests during the long lifetime of a tree. Today it is also clear that natural forms of forest management are preferable in terms of cost, as natural regeneration is much more economical than organised planting efforts.

Recent debates over biodiversity have demonstrated that extensive clear-cutting and organised planting were responsible for serious and previously unrecognised problems. These measures fundamentally altered and greatly diminished biodiversity and genetic variety in many places, greatly weakening the ability of trees to adapt to changing environmental conditions.

Waves of Deforestation

The large-scale clear-cutting that took place in European forests was the first of three major waves of deforestation in modern times. Tragically, the trees felled in this first wave did much to lay the foundations for the second, which occurred in the forests of European colonies; trees from Europe supplied the raw materials used to build the ships which made colonisation possible.

The second wave of deforestation, as illustrated by the case of India, was also triggered to a great extent by the demand for timber in urban areas. In India, as elsewhere, the Imperial Forest Service sought to shape the practice of forestry to suit its own designs by setting aside reserved forests. One effect of this approach was to undermine traditional communal rules governing the use of forest resources. For all practical purposes, the forests became an open access resource which could be used according to individual whim. However, history took a very different course in India. At the time of Indian independence in 1947, the country's soils were exhausted, its legal and economic institutions had broken down, and social stratification was more rigid than ever before. Moreover, India had not experienced any economic and social transformation comparable to industrialisation in Europe, which had given the forests there a chance to recover. Today Indian forests supply furniture and paper for 200 million city-dwellers, while they continue to be the source of traditional products on which more than 700 million people in rural areas depend.

The third wave of deforestation is currently raging, primarily, in tropical rainforests, but also in the old growth forests of North America and in parts of the former Soviet Union. Deforestation in these places has been made technically possible by cheap supplies of crude oil, which first began to flow to industrialised countries in the 1950s. Oil became the foundation for the development of modern consumer society, which is now being emulated at an accelerated pace even in remote areas of the world.

The age of petroleum has also given rise to an entirely new constellation of forces affecting most forests. In Central Europe, revenues from unprocessed timber have been declining since the 1960s. Inexpensive sources of energy for industry and transport have made iron, concrete and artificial substances more attractive and have also made it possible to import cheap timber which is clear-cut in the North as well as in the tropics. Today the rate of timber consumption in Central Europe is far below the rate of regeneration, and timber reserves continue to grow. But forests in this region are now facing a new threat which comes primarily from the pollution caused by excessive burning of fossil fuels.

In the tropics, governmental measures, which are virtually identical in most countries, are the greatest driving force behind this third wave of deforestation, which is having a heavy impact on rainforests. Expropriation by central governments of the traditional rights enjoyed by local people, which goes hand-in-hand with the advancement of private economic interests, has once again become a central issue. In the name of progress and national welfare, governments grant felling rights under conditions which are irresistible to enterprises that aim to maximise profits. Forests become disposable landscapes under such conditions, especially in areas such as Latin America, where land appears to offer a chance to produce cash crops for the national or the global market. Trees, which constitute an obstacle in the eyes of speculators, are summarily burned off. But the thin layer of humus in tropical forests is soon exhausted, at which point speculative capital moves on in its search for new frontiers of exploitation.

As external forces penetrate habitats where people base their livelihood on forest resources, new conflicts continue to develop. Even the most remote parts of the rainforest are inhabited, whether by indigenous peoples such as the Amerindians and Dayaks, or those who arrived later, such as the rubber tappers of Amazonia. These people use a variety of fruits, resins, nuts, oils, fibres and other products which can be gathered in the forest. Their use of resources is by and large sustainable, because the forest is their home and not merely one of many places which they have chosen to exploit for profit.

Conditions in the rainforests are made worse by the attempts of national governments to compensate for political negligence. Fragile rainforest ecosystems are expected to alleviate the pent-up problems of economic deprivation and social conflict which develop in more fertile regions of the country. These problems, which arise because ownership of fertile land is concentrated in the hands of fewer and fewer people, may occur as the result of obstructed land reform, as in Brazil, or secondary landlessness, as in Costa Rica.

Once these conditions develop, hunger and poverty also play a role in deforestation. When people are relocated or forced into a new environment with which they are unfamiliar, and where their modest living conditions are continually threatened because they have no rights (or because the government is too corrupt to guarantee their rights), far more forestland is destroyed than would be necessary to ensure their survival.

Rash and precipitous opening of rainforests to 'development' results in enormous social and economic damage. Although such development generates fees and taxes, the damage done to the environment, and especially to the social climate, far exceeds the value of these revenues. People who consider themselves civilised turn into robber barons when pursuing their economic interests in areas far removed from cities, where an atmosphere of latent violence is created by greed.

Asserting Local Rights and Resisting Usurpation

The history of forest farmers in the Black Forest shows that individual communities can succeed in opposing intervention by higher authorities, and even in resisting powerful market forces. It is notable that near-natural, high-quality forests often survive in such communities.

Today the victims of the second and third waves of deforestation are defending themselves with growing conviction. Local resistance is on the rise in many marginal areas where the effects of centralisation and global economic penetration are now being felt. While news of protests in the Himalayas and Amazonia has spread throughout the world, many people, such as the 'Women Under the Acacia Tree' in Kenya, have shown that very quiet forms of protest can also be effective. People everywhere who resist current global trends are concerned about protecting their traditional habitats from expropriation by outside forces. Groups in civil society and non-governmental organisations often play an important role in advocating the rights to which local people are entitled. These groups are frequently rooted in the urban world, as if in unconscious atonement for the crimes which the city has long committed against the countryside and the forest.

Local empowerment, rather than central control, is the first step towards long-term preservation of natural resources and the environment. In today's interconnected global world, even the humblest tree will soon have economic value. Only people whose rights have been guaranteed, and who also have their own resource base as well as established communal guidelines for conflict resolution, will be able to defend themselves against the selfish designs of outside forces and local elites.

Progress towards the 'new village' where these conditions prevail will involve narrowing the gap between decision-making power and accountability: those who take decisions must also be prepared to accept the consequences, whether positive or negative. Only structures designed to operate at local and regional levels can prevent the degradation of resources which are necessary for survival and which also produce long-term economic benefits. Regions with such well-balanced conditions will also be in the best position to satisfy national and international demand, as the Chagga on Kilimanjaro have clearly demonstrated.

Many governments, however, still stubbornly adhere to the principle of central control of resources. This allows the entrenched interests of social elites and forest services to prevail, and prevents rural people from promoting their interests and exercising their rights. Nevertheless, the first halting steps towards the 'new village' have begun to bear fruit. This is true even in India, where conflicts from the colonial era which remained unresolved after independence have severely crippled the full potential of forest management. Nevertheless, it will take a great deal of time to reshape Indian society along different lines, since the principles of the 'new village' not only undermine traditional gender roles but are also a threat to India's hierarchical social structure and its centralised forestry administration.

Nepal has made impressive progress in centring the use of forest resources upon local people. Forest policy in this small Himalayan country is now characterised by a level of bold innovation unmatched virtually anywhere in the world. Since the early 1990s, the government has entrusted small groups of resource users in the foothills with sustainable forest management. Forest resources are fully at the disposal of these groups.

Initial results with this approach have been encouraging. One example is evidence of rich natural regeneration wherever locally negotiated rules to protect the forest have begun to take effect. Yet even here, the road to greater social harmony will be long and fraught with conflict. Previous experience indicates that rural elites often prevail within local groups of resource users, to the disadvantage of women and members of the lower castes. In addition, some forestry officials have interpreted their changed roles as advisers rather than policemen as a loss of power.

The example of Amazonia, where there is a lack of the political stability and the administrative authority needed to guarantee respect for the law, shows how difficult it is to establish a stable economy once exploitation and violence have taken root. While government intervention often has catastrophic effects on untouched forests and their inhabitants, government services are urgently needed in regions which have been ravaged by speculation. Such regions require good schools, training facilities, financial services, and roads which can be used even in the rainy season. Only then can a permanent cultural landscape develop, characterised in part by a well-regulated use of forest resources.

Productive Forestry

Foresters have always had a preference for solving problems with technical measures. However, there is no point in planting trees before carefully weeding through legal and social thickets. Wherever forests are being degraded as the result of classic social conflicts, foresters must first learn to deal with human beings. There is a need for foresters with a sense of solidarity, who are willing to work at the margins of society to promote the well-being of people as well as the health of the natural environment. Political conditions must be basically stable before trees have a chance to flourish and technical forestry and agroforestry measures can be productive.

Agroforestry, which can foster intensified land use and also relieve pressure on existing forests, holds great promise for countries in the South. The examples of Tanzania, Kenya and Nepal show that population growth and intensification of agriculture, rather than excluding trees from the cultural landscape, have had precisely the opposite effect. Trees supply a multitude of products, restore soil fertility and have a beneficial impact on the microclimate. In future, it will be necessary not simply to breed species which produce the greatest possible yields, but to determine what combinations of flora and fauna are suited to smallholder societies and the market opportunities open to them.

There is also a need to revise forestry practices. As European foresters once advocated spruce and pine as the 'potatoes of the forest', the international forestry community today advocates planting a variety of exotic species, which are now being introduced in more or less appropriate climatic belts around

the world. If exotics are planted on degraded soils as a first step towards preparing the terrain for indigenous species, this approach may be justified. But in many places natural forests are cleared to make space for monocultures of exotics simply because they promise quick profits. Wherever this happens, countries in the South are destined to repeat the history of developments in the North, where clear-cutting of original forests resulted in a loss of social and biological niches. Moreover, the increased incidence of problems with pests has served as a further reminder that nature cannot be outwitted, even in the South.

The less obtrusive human interventions are, and the closer to nature, the more stable forests will be. In turn, ecological stability leads to a range of forest products and a more diverse forest composition. Any feasible plan to preserve genetic variety, diversity of species and rare environments must acknowledge the reality of small-scale dynamics at the village level. On the other hand, consideration must also be given to vast protected areas and reserved forests where extensive resource use is important to communities in which hunting and gathering play a vital role.

It should not be forgotten that indigenous populations have made a decisive contribution to biodiversity in tropical forests through slash-and-burn techniques and through shifting cultivation at specific sites.[3] As long as felling is selective or confined to a small scale, and as long as substantial islands of natural forestland survive nearby and can be used by flying foxes and other seed-bearers to augment plant diversity in cut-over areas, the forest will retain its ability to recover, even in the tropics.

A New Framework for the Future

In this concluding chapter I have described the three forest-preserving mechanisms upon which my personal hopes for the world's forests are based. One is local resistance to exploitation and destruction by outside forces. The second is the often underestimated natural capacity of forest vegetation to regenerate. And the third is the art of near-natural forest management, whose potential is far from fulfilled in many places where the political and social climate is not sufficiently conducive to forestry.

But do these three forces constitute a sufficient guarantee that trees will reappear where they do not exist today? If additional sectors of the population in the South are to be saved from impoverishment, and if pressure on natural resources is to be reduced, structural change on a scale comparable to that which transformed European society – and which received most of the credit for the subsequent miracle of the return of trees there – will also have to take place in the South.

Copying the 'developed' lifestyle of the North, which is based on non-renewable sources of energy, is now a major trend in the South. Attempts to aspire to the standards of industrialised countries have combined with population growth and increasing migration to create many new black holes which devour energy. Today, even the spiritual traditions of Hinduism, Buddhism and Confucianism are being increasingly obscured by the force of materialism.

The culture of extravagance in the North is a deceptive model, however, since it cannot be sustained on a global basis. Gandhi once offered a striking illustration of this by asking, 'If England has to exploit half of the world in order to be what it is, how many worlds would India need to exploit?' Today, average annual per capita consumption of crude oil in Japan is 3500 litres, compared to 600 in China. But if China's 1250 million people were to consume crude oil at the current Japanese rate, global reserves would soon be exhausted. In a full world, conflicts over distribution can no longer be neutralised by consumption of non-renewable and rapidly diminishing resources.

Here lies the real challenge for those countries and sectors of society which consider themselves 'developed': to discover and pursue a lifestyle that is appropriate for people the world over, and that does not ravage the earth and its resources. We must institute a universal culture of sustainability in which all people have access to natural resources and the chance to earn a livelihood. Hope for the world's forests will grow in proportion to the progress we make on the long road towards these goals.

Chapter 1: Switzerland

1   Hauser, 1966, p. 881.
2   Cf. Pfister, 1986b, p. 381.
3   Pfister and Schüle, 1989, p. 41.
4   Pfister, 1992, p. 40.
5   Pfister, 1990, p. 44.
6   Balsiger, 1925, p. 7.
7   Kasthofer, 1850, p. 238.
8   Sachs, 1990, p. 42.
9   Kasthofer, 1822a, p. 277.
10 Kasthofer, 1850, p. 233.
11 Kasthofer, 1850, p 227.
12 Cf. Stuber, 1993, p. 61.
13 Bill, 1992, p. 96, comment 9 (p. 239).
14 Kasthofer, 1850, p. 221.
15 Kasthofer, 1833, p. 26.
16 Hess, 1940, p. 2.
17 Kasthofer, 1850, p. 221.
18 Küchli, 1994a, p. 658.
19 von Erlach, 1944, p. 13.
20 Kasthofer, 1822b, p. 24.
21 Kasthofer, 1851, p. 7.
22 Cf. Sieferle, 1990.
23 Pfister, 1990, p. 45.
24 Pfister, 1991, p. 359.
25 Fankhauser, 1893, p. 76.
26 Kasthofer, 1828, II, p. 97.
27 Cf. Stuber, 1993, p. 111.
28 Kasthofer, 1818, p. 71.
29 Fankhauser, 1893, p. 91. This law made it possible to dissolve the right for animals to graze in the forest by making a payment equal to twenty times the estimated annual value of this right.
30 Grossmann, 1949, p. 63.
31 Stuber, 1993, p. 74.
32 Ibid., 1993, p. 111.
33 Ibid., 1993, p. 113.
34 Ibid., 1993, p. 112.
35 Fankhauser, 1856, p 132.
36 Hauser, 1968, p. 427.
37 Minutes of a meeting of the Swiss Forestry Society (SFV), 1865, p. 39 ff.
38 Keel, 1859, p. 35.
39 Cf. Küchli, 1992, p. 98 ff.
40 Kasthofer, 1833, p. 33.
41 Ibid. p. 34.
42 Fankhauser, 1856, p. 139.
43 Stuber, 1993, Figure 2.
44 Pfister, 1995, p. 86.
45 Vontobel, 1994, p. 14.
46 Cf. Küchli, 1994b.
47 Fir: *Abies alba*; Spruce: *Picea abies*.
48 von Weizsäcker and Hennicke, 1994, p. 23.
49 Voss, 1994, p. 33.

References

Balsiger, R (1925) 'Forstmeister Kasthofer und seine Zeit' *Schweiz Z Forstwes* 76, 1: pp1–10, 40–54, 66–75, 96–108.

Bill, R (1992) *Die Entwicklung der Wald- und Holznutzung in den Waldungen der Burgergemeinde Bern vom Mittelalter bis 1798*. Diss. ETH Nr 9626.

Fankhauser, F (1856) 'Über die Ursachen der Entwaldung und die Mittel, welche im bernischen Oberland degegen in den letzten Jahren angewendet wurden' *Schweiz Z Forstwes*, 7, 6: pp129–140.

Fankhauser, F (1893) *Geschichte des bernischen Forstwesens*. Bern: Stämpfli.

Grossmann, H (1949) 'Forstgesetzgebung und Forstwirtschaft in der ersten Hälfte des 19. Jahrhunderts. 1803–1848' *Beih Zeitschr Schweiz Forstwes* Nr 25.

Hauser, A (1966) 'Zur Bedeutung Karl Kasthofers für die schweizerische Forstwirtschaft und Forstgeschichte des 19 und 20 Jahrhunderts' *Schweiz Z Forstwes* 117, 12: pp879–897.

Hauser, A (1968) 'Land- und Forstwirtschaft im Wallis vor und nach der industriellen Revolution' *Agrarpolitische Revue* 24: pp422–429.

Kasthofer, K (1818) *Benerkungen über die Wälder des Bernischen Hochgebirges*. Aarau: Sauerländer.

Kasthofer, K (1822a) *Bemerkungen auf einer Alpen-Reise über den Brünig, Bragel, Kirenzenberg, und über die Flüela, den Maloya und Splügen*. Aarau: Sauerländer.

Kasthofer, K (1822b) *Bemerkungen auf einer Alpenreise über den Susten, Bernardin, und über die Oberalp, Furka und Grimsel*. Aarau: Sauerländer.

Kashofer, K (1828) *Der Lehrer im Walde*. Teile I und II. Bern: Jenni.

Kashofer, K (1833) *Betrachtungen über die einheimischen Eisenwerke und über die Freiheit der Holzausfuhr*. Bern: Huber.

Kasthofer, K (1850) 'Die Forstverwaltung und Bewirtschaftung der freien Staatswälder im bernischen Hochgebirge' *Schweiz Z Forstwes* 2, 1: pp7–15.

Keel, J (1859) *Bericht über die forstlichen Zustände im Kantone Appenzell A Rh* Bühler 1860.

Küchli, Ch (1992) *Wurzein und Visionen – Promenaden durch den Schweizer Wald*. Aarau: AT.

Küchli, Ch (1994a) 'Die forstliche Vergangenheit in den Schweizer Bergen: Erinnerungen an die aktuelle Situation in den Ländern des Südens' *Schweiz Z Forstwes* 145, 8: pp647–667.

Küchli, Ch (1994b) *Berner Wald wohin? Grundlagenbericht zur Schaffung des neuen Berner Waldgesetzes*. Bern: Amt für Wald und Natur.

Marchand, X (1849) *Über die Enwaldung der Gebirge. Denkschrift an die Direktion des Innern des Kantons Bern*. Herausgegeben von der jurassischen Nacheiferungsgesellschaft (Société jurassienne d'émulation), Porrentruy. Bern 1849.

Pfister, Chr (1986) 'Bevölkerung, Wirtschaft und Ernährung in den Berg-und Talgebieten des Kantons Bern 1760–1860' *Itinera, Fasc* 5/6: pp361–391.

Pfister, Chr (1990) 'The Early Loss of Ecological Stability in an Agrarian Region' in Brimblecombe, P & Pfister, Chr *The Silent Countdown. Essays in European Environmental History*. Berlin: Springer.

Pfister, Chr (1991) 'Ernährungslandschaften vor dem Zeitalter der Eisenbahn' in Stälhelin, H B *Dritter Schweizerischer Ernährungsbericht*. Bern: Bundesamt für Gesundheitswesen.

Pfister, Chr (1992) '800 Jahre Umweltgeschichte am Beispiel des Kantons Bern' *Mitt Naturf Ges Bern* 49: pp35–48.

Pfister, Chr (1995) *Das 1950er Syndrom. Der Weg in die Konsumgesellschaft*. Bern: Haupt.

Pfister, Chr & Schüle, H (1989) 'Metaquellen als Grundlagen zur Abgrenzung un Typisierung jistorischer Agragzonen. Das Beispiel des Kantons Bern im späten 18 und 19. Jahrhundert' *Itinera*, 10: pp28–57.

Protokoll, Sitzungen des SFV 1865 (Referat Staatsrat von Riedmatten). Schweiz Z Forstwes 16 (1866): p17–22, 31–42. Minutes of a meeting of the Swiss Society of Foresters (remarks by Councillor von Riedmatten).

Sachs, W (1990) 'On the Archaeology of the Development Idea' *The Ecologist*, 20, 2: pp42–43.

Sieferle, R P (1990) 'The Energy System – A Basic Concept of Environmental History' in Brimblecombe, P & Pfister, Chr (Eds) *The Silent Countdown. Essays in European Environmental History*. Berlin, New York: Springer.

Stuber, M (1993) *Anweisungen zu einer besseren Oekonomie der Wälder. Nachhaltigkeitskonzept im Kanton Bern 1750–1880*. Bern: MA thesis, Faculty of History, University of Bern.

von Erlach (1994) 'Karl Albrecht Kasthofer' *Beiheft zu den Zeitschriften des Schweizerischen Forstvereins* Nr 22.

Vontobel, W (1994) 'Der Preis der Natur' *Panda Magazin* 27, 4. Zürich: WWF Schweiz.

Voss, A (1994) 'Die Zukunft gestalten: Gedanken zur Energiefrage' in *Zehnmal Zehn Atel-Jahre*. Olten: Aare-Tessin AG für Elektrizität.

Weizsäcker, E U von & Hennicke, P (1994) 'Der Effizienzmarkt als Herausforderung für Energieversorgungsunternehmen im Jahrhundert der Umwelt' in *Zehnmal Zehn Atel-Jahre*. Olten: Aare-Tessin AG für Elektrizität.

Chapter 2: India

1   Dowson, 1984, p. 108.
2   *Quercus incana.*
3   Pandey and Singh, 1984, p. 50.
4   Moench, 1988, p. 127.
5   Moench and Bandyopadhyay, 1985, p. 127.
6   Shah, 1994, p. 18.
7   *Shorea robusta.*
8   Tucker, 1983, p. 150.
9   Guha, 1988, p. 285 .
10 Tucker, 1983. p. 156.
11 *Cedrus deodar.*
12 Tucker, 1983, p. 157.
13 Ibid, p. 159.
14 Ibid, p. 159.
15 Guha, 1988, p. 287.
16 Tucker, 1983, p. 157.
17 Gadgil and Guha, 1992, p. 123.
18 Cf. Guha, 1988, p. 287.
19 Gadgil, 1991, p. 38.
20 Hesmer, 1975, p. 67.
21 Cf. Kulkarni, 1983, p 86.
22 Hesmer, 1975, p. 67.
23 Guha, 1988, p. 288.
24 Shyamsunder and Parameswarappa, 1987, p. 334.
25 Guha, 1988, p. 290.
26 *Pinus roxburghii.*
27 Guha, 1988, p. 289.
28 Cf. Guha, 1988, p. 292, and Tucker, 1988, p. 97.
29 Cf. Tucker, 1983, p. 164.
30 Cf. Hardin, 1968.
31 Weber, 1987, p. 617.
32 Cf. Weber, 1989, p. 30 ff.
33 Shah, 1994, p. 11.
34 Weber, 1989, p. 33.
35 Weber, 1989, p. 41.
36 Bhatt, 1980, p. 12.
37 Mishra and Tripathi, 1978, p. 27.
38 Saxena, 1991, p. 30.
39 Shah, 1994, p. 8.
40 Weber, 1989, p. 112.
41 Bänziger, 1991.
42 Cf. Campbell, 1996.
43 Campbell and Denholm, 1993, p. 6 ff.
44 Cf. Khosla, 1994.
45 See, for example, Sharma, 1994.
46 Imhof, 1988, p. 236.
47 Cf. Rangan, 1993.
48 Weber, 1987, p. 627.
49 Shah, 1994, p. 18.
50 Pachauri, 1992, p. 2.
51 Cf. Gadgil and Guha, 1994.

References

Agarwal, A & Chak, A (Ed) (1991) *Floods, Flood Plains and Environmental Myths, State of India's Environment 3*. New Delhi: Centre for Science and Environment.

Bänziger, A (1991) '"Umarmt die Bäume", lautete die Devise' *Zürich: Tages-Anzeiger*, 10 December 1991.

Bhatt, Ch P (1980) *Ecosystem of the Central Himalayas and Chipko Movement*. Gopeshar: Dashauli Gram Swarajya Sangh.

Campbell, J G & Denholm, J (1993) *Inspirations in Community Forestry. Report of the Seminar on Himalayan Community Forestry, Kathmandu, Nepal*, 1–4 June 1992. Kathmandu: ICIMOD.

Campbell, J Y (1996) 'The Power to Control Versus the Need to Use: A Pragmatic View of Joint Forest Management' *Community Property Resource Digest*, No 37: pp9–10.

Dowson, J (1984) *A Classical Dictionary of Hindu Mythology and Religion, Geography, History and Literature*. Calcutta: Rupa.

Gadgil, M & Guha, R (1991) 'Deforestation: Problems and Prospects' in Rawat, A S (1991) *History of Forestry in India*. New Delhi: Indus Publishing Company.

Gadgil, M & Guha, R (1992) *This Fissured Land. An Ecological History of India*. Delhi: Oxford University Press.

Gadgil, M & Guha, R (1994) 'Ecological Conflicts and the Environmental Movement in India' in Ghai, D (1994) *Development and Environment. Sustaining People and Nature*. Oxford/Geneva: Blackwell/UNRISD.

Guha, R (1988) 'Forestry and Social Protest in British Kumaun, c 1893–1921' in Fortmann, L & Bruce, J W (1988) *Whose Trees? Property Dimensions in Forestry*. Boulder: Westview Press.

Hesmer, H (1975) *Leben und Werk von Dietrich Brandis, 1824–1907* Opladen: Westdeutscher Verlag.

Hardin, G (1968) 'The Tragedy of the Commons' *Science* 162: pp1243–1248.

Imhof, A E (1988) *Die Lebenszeit. Vom aufgeschobenen Tod und von der Kunst des Lebens*. München: Beck.

Khosla, A (1994) 'Sustainable National Development. Independent Sector Organisations' *Development Alternatives*, 4, 3: pp1–4.

Kulkarni, S (1983) 'The Forest Policy and the Forest Bill: A Critique and Suggestions for Change' in Fernandes, W & Kulkarni, S *Towards a New Forest Policy. People's Rights and Environmental Needs*. New Delhi: Indian Social Institute.

Mishra, A & Tripathi, S (1978) *Chipko Movement*. New Delhi: Gandhi Book House.

Moench, M & Bandyopadhyay, J (1985) 'Local Needs and Forest Resource Management in the Himalayas' in Bandyopadhyay, J, Jayal, N D, Schoettli, U & Singh, Ch (1985) *India's Environment. Crisis and Responses*. Dehra Dun: Natraj Publishers.

Moench, M (1988) '"Turf" and Forest Management in a Garhwal Hill Village (India)' in Fortmann, L & Bruce, J W *Whose Trees?: Proprietary Dimensions of Forestry*. Boulder: Westview Press.

Pachauri, R K (1992) 'Energy and Environmental Issues in Sustainable Development of Mountain Areas: Development or Destruction?' in Monga, P & Ramana, P V *Energy, Environment and Sustainable Development in the Himalayas*. New Delhi: Indus Publishing Company.

Pandey, U & Singh, J S (1984) 'Energy-flow Relationships Between Agro- and Forest Ecosystems in Central Himalaya' *Environmental Conservation* 11, 1: pp45–53.

Rangan, H (1993) 'Romancing the Environment. Popular Environmental Action in the Garhwal Himalayas' in Friedmann, J & Rangan, H *In Defense of Livelihood. Comparative Studies on Environmental Action*. West Hartford, Conn: Kumarian Press/UNRISD.

Saxena, N C (1991) 'Forest Policy in India: A Critique and an Alternative Framework' *Wastelands News*, Aug–Oct 1991.

Shah, S A (1994) 'Silvicultural Management of Our Forests' *Wastelands News*, 9, 2: pp8–30.

Sharma, R (1994) 'Learning from Experiences of Joint Forest Management in india' *Forest, Trees and People Newsletter*, No 24, june 1994.

Shyamsunder, S & Parameswarappa, S (1987) 'Forestry in India – the Forester's View' *Ambio*, 16, 6: pp332–337.

Tucker, R P (1983) 'The British Colonial System and the Forests of the Western Himalayas, 1815–1914' in Tucker, R P & Richards, J F *Global Deforestation and the Nineteenth-Century World Economy*. Durham, N C: Duke Press Policy Studies.

Tucker, R P (1988) 'The British Empire and India's Forest Resources: The Timberlands of Assam and Kumaon, 1914–1950' in Richards, J F & Tucker, R P *World Deforestation in the Twentieth Century*. Durham and London: Duke University Press.

Weber, T (1987) 'Is There Still a Chipko Andolan?' *Pacific Affairs*, 60, 4: pp615–628.

Weber, T (1989) *Hugging the Trees. The Story of the Chipko Movement*. New Delhi: Penguin.

Chapter 3: Nepal

1   Küchli, 1988.
2   Cf. Mahat, Griffin and Shepherd, 1987; Pandey, 1982.
3   Banyan: *Ficus bengalensis*; pipal: *Ficus religiosa*.
4   Cf. Ives and Messerli, 1989.
5   Cf. World Bank, 1979.
6   Estimate for 1981; cf. Ives and Messerli, 1989, p. 35.
7   Cf. Högger, 1993, p., 192.
8   Cf. Gilmour and Fisher, 1991, p. 26.
9   Cf. Manandhar, 1982.
10 Cf. Küchli, 1988, p. 84.
11 *Pinus patula*.
12 Chilauna: *Schima wallichii*; Katus: *Castanopsis Spp.*
13 Campbell and Denholm, 1993, p. 8.
14 Personal communication with Patrick Robinson,. May 22,1993.
15 English, 1985, p. 69.
16 Bista, 1991, p. 26.
17 *Santalum album*.
18 Cf. especially Ives and Messerli, 1989.
19 Cf. H. Gurung, 1989.
20 Gilmour and Fisher, 1991, p. 23.
21 Cf. Campbell, 1983; Cambell, Shrestha and Euphrat, 1987; Mahat, 1985.
22 Cf. Baral, 1991.
23 Cf. Gilmour and Nurse, 1991.
24 Talbott and Khadka, 1994, p. 8,9.
25 Bänziger, 1990.
26 Cf. Banskota, 1989, p. 5.
27 Cf. Malla, 1992.
28 Robinson and Joshi, 1993, p. 104.
29 Cf. Carlson, 1985.
30 S.M. Gurung, 1989, p. 358.
31 Kienholz, Hafner and Schneider, 1984.

References

Agarwal, A & Chak, A (Ed) (1991) *Floods, Flood Plains and Environmental Myths. State of India's Environment 3*. New Delhi: Centre for Science and Environment.

Banskota, M (1989) *Hill Agriculture and the Wilder Market Economy: Transformation Processes and Experience of the Bagmati Zone in Nepal*. ICIMOD Occasional Papers No 10.

Baral, J Ch (1991) *Indigenous Forestry Activities in Achham District of Far Western Hills Nepal*. Kathmandu: Community Forestry Development Project.

Bänziger, A (1990) 'Ueberleben in Nepal' *Zürich: Tages-Anzeiger*, 22 June 1990, p65.

Bista, D B (1991) *Fatalism and Development. Nepal's Struggle for Moderistaion. 3rd Impression 1992*. Hyderabad: Orient Longman.

Campbell, J G (1983) *People and Forests in Hill Nepal*. CFDP, Field Document No 10.

Campbell, J G, Shrestha, R J & Euphrat, F (1987) 'Socio-economic Factors in Traditional Forest Use and management' in *Banko Janakari* 1, 4: pp45–54.

Campbell, G J & Denholm, J (1993) *Inspirations in Community Forestry. Report of the Seminar on Himalayan Community Forestry, Kathmandu, Nepal, 1–4 June 1992*. Kathmandu: ICIMOD.

Carson, B (1985) *Erosion and Sedimentation Processes in the Nepalese Himalaya*. ICIMOD Occasional Paper No 1.

English, R (1985) 'Himalayan State Formation and the Impact of British Rule in the Nineteenth Century' *Mountain Research and Development* 5, 1: pp61–78.

Gilmour, D A & Fisher, R J (1991) *Villagers, Forests and Foresters. The Philosophy, Process and Practice of Community Forestry in Nepal*. Kathmandu: Sahayogi Press.

Gilmour, D A & Nurse, M C (1991) 'Farmer Initiatives in Increasing Tree Cover in Central Nepal' *Mountain Research and Development* 11, 4: pp329–337.

Gurung, H (1989) *Regional Patterns of Migration in Nepal*. Papers of the East–West Population Institute, Honolulu.

Gurung, S M (1989) 'Human Perception of Mountain Hazards in the Kakani–Kathmandu area: Experiences from the Middle Mountains of Nepal' *Mountain Research and Development* 9, 4: pp353–364.

Högger, R (1993) *Wasserschlange und Sonnenvogel. Die andere Seite der Entwicklungshilfe*. Frauenfeld: Waldgut.

Ives, J D & Messerli, B (1989) *The Himalayan Dilemma. Reconciling Development and Conservation*. London, New York: Routledge.

Kienholz, H, Hafner, H & Schneider, G (1984) 'Stability, Instability and Conditional Instability. Mountain Ecosystem Concepts based on a Field Survey of the Kakani Area in the Middle Hills of Nepal' *Mountain Research and Dvelopment* 4, 1: pp55–62.

Küchli, Ch (1988) 'Gemeindeforstwirtschaft in Nepal oder "Was die Wualder sonst noch nützen neben dem Holz"' *NZZ* Nr 54, pp82–84.

Mahat, T B S (1985) *Community Protection of Forest Areas: A Case Study from Chautara, Nepal*. Paper presented to the International Workshop on the Management of National Parks and Protected Areas of the Hindukusch-Himalaya, Kathmandu, 6–11 May 1985.

Mahat, T B S, Griffin, D M & Shepherd, K R (1987) 'Human Impact on Some Forests of the Middle Hills of Nepal. 4. A Detailed Study in South East Sindhu Palchok and North East Kabhre Palanchok' *Mountain Research and Development* 7, 2: pp111–134.

Malla, Y B (1992) *The Changing Role of the Forest Resource in the Hills of Nepal.* Canberra: Australian National University, PhD Thesis.

Manandhar, P K (1981) *Introduction to Policy, Legislation and Programmes of Community Forestry Development in Nepal.* CFDP, Field Document No 1a (updated June 1982).

Pandey, K (1982) *Fodder Trees and Tree Fodder in Nepal.* Berne: Swiss Development Cooperation.

Robinson, P J & Joshi, M R (1993) 'Private Forestry: Needs and Opportunities' *Banko Janakar,* 4, 1: pp103–106.

Talbott, K & Khadka, S (1994) *Handing it Over. An Analysis of the Legal and Policy Framework of Community Forestry in Nepal.* Washington: World Resources Institute.

World Bank (1979) *Nepal: Development Performance and Prospects.* Washington DC: World Bank.

Chapter 4: Tanzania

1   Lawuo, 1979, p. 13.
2   Finger millet: *Eleusine coracana.*
3   Pike, 1965, p. 94.
4   Stahl, 1964, p. 12.
5   Lawuo, 1979, p. 17.
6   Hecklau, 1989, p. 315.
7   Köhler, 1988, p. 111.
8   Hecklau, 1989, p. 157.
9   Lawuo, 1979, p. 24.
10 Stahl, 1965, p. 42.
11 Lawuo, 1979, p. 22.
12 Ibid. p. 24.
13 Acland, 1980, p. 60.
14 Kivumbi and Newmark, 1991, p. 83.
15 Cf. Boserup, 1965.
16 O'Kting'ati and Kessy, 1991, p. 73.
17 Cf. Fernandes, O'Kting'ati, and Maghembe, 1984.
18 Yam: *Dioscorea alata, D. bulbifera.*
19 Queme: *Telfairia pedata.*
20 Msesewe: *Rauvolfia caffra.*
21 African dragon-tree: *Dracaena afromontana.*
22 Maro, 1988, p. 281.
23 *Colocasia esculenta.*
24 O'Kting'ati and Kessy, 1991, p. 76.
25 Ibid., p. 71, 72.
26 Cf. Egger, 1983, p. 572.
27 Warner, 1993, p. 168.
28 Güntert, 1995, p. 9.
29 Baumgartner, 1996.
30 Cf. Raikes, 1986, p. 122.
31 Warner, 1993, p., 19.
32 Gamassa, 1991, p. 7; p. 1.
33 Fernandes, O'Kting'ati and Maghembe, 1984, p. 82.
34 Cf. Maro, 1988, p. 281.
35 Cf. Lamprey, Michelmore and Lamprey, 1991.
36 O'Kting'ati and Kessy, 1991, p. 80.
37 Warner, 1993, p. 169.
38 Berry, 1993, p. 538; Gamassa, 1991, p. 1.
39 Raikes, 1986, p. 127.
40 Ibid., p. 128.
41 Boesen, Havnevik, Koponen, and Odgaard, 1986, p., 19.
42 Cf. Bruijnzeel and Proctor, 1995.
43 Pócs, 1991, p. 32.
44 Sarmett and Faraji, 1991, p. 62.

References

Acland, J D (1980) *East African Crops. An Introduction to the Production of Field and Plantation Crops in Kenya, Tanzania and Uganda.* London: Longman.

Baumgartner, P (1996) 'Der Mühlstein hängt schwer am Hals. Vom Gipfel der G-7 werden Anstösse zur Entschuldung der Drittweltländer erwartet' *Zürich: Tages-Anzeiger,* 27 June 1996.

Berry, L, Lewis, L A & Williams, C (1990) 'East African Highlands' in Turner, B L et al *The Earth as Transformed by Human Action.* Cambridge: Cambridge University Press.

Boesen, J, Havnevik, K J, Koponen, J & Odgaard, R (1986) *Tanzania. Crisis and Struggle for Survival.* Uppsala: Scandinavian Institute of African Studies.

Boserup, E (1965) *The Conditions of Agricultural Growth.* London: Allen & Unwin.

Bruijnzeel, L A & Proctor, J (1995) 'Hydrology and Biogeochemistry of tropical Montane Cloud Forests: What Do We Really Know?' in Hamilton, L S, Juvik, J O & Scatena, F N (1995) *Tropical Montane Cloud Forests.* New York: Springer.

Egger, K (1983) 'Oekologischer Landbau in den Tropen' *Umschau,* 19: pp569–573.

Fernandes, E C M, O'Kting'ati, A & Maghembe, J (1984) 'The Chagga Homegardens: A Multistoreyed Agroforestry Cropping System on Mt Kilimanjaro (Northern Tanzania)' *Agroforestry Systems,* 2: pp73–86.

Gamassa, D M (1991) 'Historical Change in Human Population on Mount Kilimanjaro and its Implications' in Newmark, W D *The Conservation of Mount Kilimanjaro.* Gland: IUCN.

Güntert, B (1995) 'Ein SAP kommt selten allein. Strukturanpassungsprogramm in Tansania' *Entwicklung & Developpement,* 45: pp8–11.

Hecklau, H (1989) *Ostafrika. Wissenschaftliche Länderkunden Bd 33.* Darmstadt: Wissenschaftliche Buchgesellschaft.

Kivumbi, C O & Newmark, W D (1991) 'The History of the half-mile forestry strip on Mount Kilimanjaro' in Newmark, W D *The Conservation of Mount Kilimanjaro.* Gland: IUCN.

Köhler, M (1988) *Ostafrika.* Köln: DuMont.

Lamprey, R H, Michelmore, F & Lamprey, H F (1991) 'Changes in the Boundary of the Montane Rainforest on Mount Kilimanjaro between 1958 and 1987' in Newmark, W D *The Conservation of Mount Kilimanjaro.* Gland: IUCN.

Lawuo, Z E (1979) *Education and Social Change in a Rural Community. A Study of Colonial Education and Local Response among the Chagga Between 1920 and 1945.* Dar es Salaam University Press.

Maro, P S (1988) 'Agricultural Land Management under Population Pressure: the Kilimanjaro Experience, Tanzania' *Mountain Research and Development,* 8, 4: pp273–282.

O'Kting'ati, A & Kessy, J F (1991) 'The Farming Systems on Mount Kilimanjaro' in Newmark, W D *The Conservation of Mount Kilimanjaro*. Gland: IUCN.

Pike, A G (1965) 'Kilimanjaro and the Furrow Systems' *Tanganyika Notes and Records*, 64: pp95–96.

Pócs, T (1991) 'The Significance of Lower Plants in the Conservation of Mount Kilimanjaro' in Newmark, W D *The Conservation of Mount Kilimanjaro*. Gland: IUCN.

Raikes, P (1986) 'Eating the Carrot and Wielding the Stick: The Agricultural Sector in Tanzania' in Boessen, J, Havnevik, K J, Koponen, J & Odgaard, R *Tanzania. Crisis and Struggle for Survival*. Uppsala: Scandinavian Institute of African Studies.

Sarmett, J D & Faraji, S A (1991) 'The Hydrology of Mount Kilimanjaro: An Examination of Dry Season Runoff and Possible Factors Leading to its Decrease' in Newmark, W D *The Conservation of Mount Kilimanjaro*. Gland: IUCN.

Stahl, K M (1964) *History of the Chagga People of Kilimanjaro*. The Hague: Mouton & Co.

Stahl, K M (1965) 'Outline of Chagga History' *Tanganyika Notes and Records*, 64: pp35–49.

Warner, K (1993) *Patterns of Farmer tree growing in Eastern Africa: A Socioeconomic Analysis*. Oxford Forestry Institute, Tropical Forestry Papers 27.

Chapter 5: Kenya

1   Heyer, 1990, p. 106-107.
2   Cf. Hoekstra, 1987, p. 325.
3   Nzioki, 1982, p. 1.
4   *Xanthosoma sagittifolium*.
5   A poisonous paste was concocted from the leaves and twigs of the evergreen *Acakanthera schimperi*.
6   Nzoiki, 1982, p. 28.
7   Ibid., 1982, p. 16.
8   Hecklau, 1989, p. 164; Pestalozzi, 1986, p. 106.
9   O'Leary, 1984, p. 35.
10 Cf. Warner, 1993, p. 35.
11 Cf. Dewees, 1993, p. 15.
12 Cf. Rocheleau, 1987.
13 Teel, 1988, p. 78.
14 Cf. Rao and Westley, 1989, p. 11.
15 Cf. Scherr, 1989, p. 12.
16 Muvingo, or mpingo (*Dalbergia melanoxylon*); see Teel, 1988, p. 84.
17 Cf. Maathai, 1988, p. 23.
18 *Acacia mearnsii*; see Dewees, 1993, p. 49.
19 Cf. Scherr, 1989, p. 16.
20 *Neue Zürcher Zeitung*, 1995, Nr. 169.
21 Cf. Hoekstra, 1984, p. 12.
22 Cf. Coe, 1994.
23 Ong, 1994, p. 9; Vandenbeldt, 1990, p. 186.
24 Vandenbelt, 1990, p. 168.
25 Cf. Hoekstra, 1987, p. 326; Teel, 1988, p. 61.
26 Nair, 1993, p. 149.

References

Baumgartner, P (1995) 'Weltbank befürchet Abkoppelung. In Schwarzafrika sind umfassende Wirtschaftsreformen dringend nötig' *Zürich: Tages-Anzeiger*, 8 July 1995, p25.

Coe, R (1994) 'Through the Looking Glass: 10 Common Problems in Alley-cropping Research' *Agroforestry Today*, 6, 1: pp9–11.

Dewees, P A (1993) *Social and Economic Incentives for Smallholder Tree Growing. A Case Study from Murang'a District, Kenya*. Rome: FAO.

Hecklau, H (1989) *Ostafrika. Wissenschaftliche Luanderkunden* Bd 33. Darmstadt: Wissenschaftliche Buchgesellschaft.

Heyer, J (1990) *Kenya: Monitoring Living Conditions and Consumption Patterns*. Geneva: UNRISD.

Hoekstra, D A (1984) *Agroforestry Systems for the Semi-arid Areas of Machakos District, Kenya*. Nairobi: ICRAF, Working Paper No 19.

Hoekstra, D A (1987) 'Economics of Agroforestry Systems in Africa' in Beer, J W, Fassbender, H W & Heuveldop, J *Advances in Agroforestry Research*. Turrialba: CATIE/GTZ.

Maathai, W (1988) *The Green Belt Movement. Sharing the Approach and the Experiment*. Nairobi: Environment Liaison Centre International.

Nair, P K R (1993) *An Introduction to Agroforestry*. Dordrecht: Kluwer Academic Publishers.

Neue Zürcher Zeitung (1995) 'Kenyas Regierung erneut auf dem Prüfstand' Nr 169, p3.

Nzioki, S (1982) *Kenya's People: Akamba*. London: Evans Brothers.

O'Leary, M (1984) *The Kitui Akamba. Economic and Social Change in Semi-arid Kenya*. London: Heinemann.

Ong, C K (1994) 'Alley Cropping – Ecological Pie in the Sky?' *Agroforestry Today*, 6, 6: pp8–10.

Pestalozzi, P (1986) 'Historical and Present Day Agricultural Change on Mt Kenya' in Winiger, M *Mount Kenya Area. Contributions to Ecology and Socio-economy*. Geographica Bernensia, Vol A1, Berne.

Rao, M R & Westley, S B (1989) 'Agroforestry for Africa's Semi-arid Zone. Experience from ICRAF's Field Station' *Agroforestry Today*, 1, 1: pp5–11.

Rocheleau, D (1987) 'Woman, Trees and Tenure: Implications for Agroforestry Research and Development' in Raintree, J B *Land, Trees and Tenure: Proceedings of an International Workshop on Tenure Issues in Agroforestry*. Nairobi: ICRAF.

Scherr, S J (1989) 'The Legislative Context for Agroforestry Development in Kenya. IUFRO Working Party S4. 08-03' in *Forstwissenschaftliche Beiträge, Fachbereich Forstökonomie und Forstpolitik*, ETH Zürich, 6: pp171–194.

Teel, W (1988) *A Pocket Directory of Trees and Seeds in Kenya*. Nairobi: Kengo.

Vandenbelt, R J (1990) 'Agroforestry in the Semi-arid Tropics' in MacDcken, K G & Vergara, N T *Agroforestry: Classification and Management*. New York: John Wiley & Sons.

Warner, K (1993) *Patterns of Farmer Tree Growing in Eastern Africa: A Socioeconomic Analysis*. Oxford Forestry Institute, Tropical Forestry Papers 27.

Chapter 6: Costa Rica

1 The scientific name for the laurel is *Cordia alliodora.* See Opler and Janzen, 1983, p 219 ff.
2 Guacimo blanco: *Goethalsia meiantha;* Anonillo: *Rollinia microsepala.*
3 These oaks are *Quercus copeyensis, Q. seemannii* and *Q. costaricensis.*
4 Biesanz, 1987, p. 15.
5 Cf. Utting, 1993, p. 26.
6 Cf. Butterfield, 1994, p. 317.
7 Cf. Ghimire, 1993, p. 79.
8 Cf. Utting, 1993, p. 39.
9 Cf. Kapp, 1989.
10 Nations and Komer, 1987, p. 164; Pedroni and Flores Rodas, 1992, p. 41.
11 Cf. Anderson, 1990, p. 9.
12 Pedroni and Flores Rodas, 1992, p. 35.
13 Cf. Utting, 1993, p. 4; Butterfield, 1994, p. 322.
14 *Neue Zürcher Zeitung,* 1992, No. 152.
15 Pedroni and Flores Rodas, 1992, p. 38; *Neue Zürcher Zeitung,* 1992; No. 119.
16 Pefroni and Flores Rodas, 1992, p. 29.
17 Budowski, 1957.
18 Poró: *Erythrina poeppigiana;* Cf. Fassbender, 1994.
19 See, for example, Beer, Fassbender, and Heuveldop, 1987.
20 *Neue Zürcher Zeitung,* 1992, Nr. 146.
21 Butterfield, 1994, p. 319.
22 McDade and Hartshorn, 1994; p. 9.
23 Cf. Uhl, Buschbacher and Serrão, 1988.
24 Balsa: *Ochroma lagopus;* Cecropia: *Cecropia spp.*
25 For a recent discussion of plant succession, see McDade and Hartshorn, 1994, p. 67 ff.
26 McDade and Hartshorn, 1994, p. 8.
27 Cf. Gomez-Pompa, Vazques-Yanes and Guevara, 1972.
28 Cf. Jacobs, 1988, p. 96.
29 Cf. Sayer, McNeely and Stuart, 1990.
30 Brown and Lugo, 1990, p. 4.
31 Finegan, 1992, p. 296.
32 Howard, 1995, p. 106.
33 Ibid., p. 108.
34 *The Tico Times,* 30 March, 1990, p. 11.
35 *Neue Zürcher Zeitung,* 1992, Nr. 146.
36 Blaser and Comacho, 1991, p. 8.
37 Cf. Berner and Stadtmüller, 1988.
38 Cf. Hutchinson, 1988.
39 aus der Beek and Saenz, 1992, p. ix.
40 Cf. Berner, 1991.
41 On restoration of the nutrient balance, see Weidelt, 1993, p. 159.
42 Cf. Stadtmüller and aus der Beek, 1992.
43 Cf. Hutchinson, 1993; Finegan, Sabogal, Reiche and Hutchinson, 1993.
44 Cf. Kapp, 1993, p. 13.
45 *Neue Zürcher Zeitung,* 1995, No. 66.
46 Veillon, 1976, p. 105; Veillon, 1991; Veillon, 1992.
47 Cf. Lamprecht, 1989, p. 61.

References

Anderson, A B (Ed) (1990) *Alternatives to Deforestation: Steps Toward Sustainable Use of the Amazon Rain Forest.* New York: Columbia University Press.

aus der Beek, R & Sáenz, G (1992) 'Manejo Forestal Basado en la regeneracíon Natural del Bosque: Estudio de Caso en los Robledales de Altura de la Cordillera de Talamanca, Costa Rica' *Coleccíon Silvicultura y Manejo de Bosques Naturales No 6.* Turrialba: CATIE.

Beer, J W, Fassbender, H W & Heuveldop, J (1987) *Advances in Agroforestry Research.* Turrialba: CATIE/GTZ.

Berner, P (1991) 'Short-term Monitoring of Girth Increment of High Altitude Oaks in Costa Rica. Implications for Natural Forest Management' in *Proceedings of the ATB Meeting San Antonio.*

Berner, P & Stadtmüller, Th (1988) 'Naturnaher Waldbau in Bergwäldern der feuchten Tropen: Erfahrungen, Probleme, Perspektiven' *Schweizerische Sietschrift für Forstwesen,* 139, 12: pp1031–1044.

Biesanz, R (1987) *The Costa Ricans.* San José: EUNED.

Blaser, J & Camacho, M (1991) 'Estructura, Composición y Aspectos Silviculturales de un Bosque de Robles (Quercus spp.) del Piso Montano en Costa Rica' *Colección Silvicultura y Manejo de Bosques Naturales No 1.* Turrialba: CATIE.

Brown, S & Lugo, A E (1990) 'Tropical Secondary Forests' *Journal of Tropical Ecology,* 6: pp1–32.

Budowski, G (1957) *The Opening of Virgin Areas for Agriculture and Animal Husbandry and Some of Its Implications.* Turrialba: CATIE.

Butterfield, R P (1994) 'Forestry in Costa Rica: Status, Rsearch Priorities, and the Role of La Selva Biological Station' in McDade, L A, Bawa, K S, Hespenheide, H A & Hartshorn, G S *La Selva. Ecology and Natural History of a Neotropical Rain Forest.* Chicago: The University of Chicago Press.

Fassbender, H-W (1994) 'Agroforstliche Produktionssysteme in Costa Rica. Nachhaltige produktion und Bodenschutz' *Allgemeine Forst Zeitschrift,* 49, 26: pp1440–1444.

Finegan, B (1992) 'The Management Potential of Neotropical Secondary Lowland Rain Forest' *Forest Ecology and Management* 47: pp295–321.

Finegan, B, Sabogal, C, Reiche, C & Hutchinson, I (1993) 'Los Bosques Húmedos Tropicales de América Central: Su Manejo Sostenible es Posible y Rentable' *Revista Forestal Centroamericana,* 2, 6: pp17–27.

Ghimire, K B (1993) *Linkages between Population, Environment and Development. Case Studies from Costa Rica, Pakistan and Uganda.* Geneva: United Nations Research Institute for Social Development.

Gómez-Pompa, A, Vázques-Yanes, C & Guevara, S (1972) 'The Tropical Rain Forest: A Nonrenewable Resource' *Science,* 177: pp762–765.

Hutchinson, I D (1988) 'Points of Departure for Silviculture in Humid Tropical Forests' *Commonwealth Forestry Revue,* 67, 3: pp223–230.

Hutchinson, I (1993) 'Silvicultura y Manejo en un Bosque Secundario Tropical: Caso Pérez Zeledón, Costa Rica' *Revista Forestal Centroamericana,* 2, 2: pp13–18.

Jacobs, M (1988) *The Tropical Rain Forest* Berlin, New York: Springer.

Kapp, G (1989) *Perfil Ambiental de la Zona Baja de Talamanca, Costa Rica.* Turrialba: CATIE/GTZ/DFG.

Kapp, G (1993) 'Entwicklungsorienterte Forschung – Bäuerliche Feuchtwaldwirtschaft in den Tieflandtropen Zentralamerikas' *Enwicklung und ländlicher Raum,* 27, 3: pp11–16.

Lamprecht, H (1989) *Silviculture in the Tropics. Tropical Forest Ecosystems and Their Tree Species – Possibilities and Methods for Their Long-Term Utilisation.* Eschborn: GTZ.

McDade, L A & Hartshorn, G S (1994) 'La Selva Biological Station' in McDade, L A, Bawa, K S, Hespenheide, H A & Hartshorn, G S *La Selva. Ecology and Natural History of a Neotropical Rain Forest.* Chicago: The University of Chicago Press.

Howard, A F (1995) 'Price Trends for Stumpage and Selected Agricultural Products in Costa Rica' *Forest Ecology and Management,* 75: pp101–110.

Nations, J D & Komer, D I (1987) 'Rainforests and the Hamburger Society' *The Ecologist,* 17, 4/5: pp161–167.

Neue Zürcher Zeitung (1992) 'Wald als Unwert in Costa Rica' Nr 19: p5..

Neue Zürcher Zeitung (1992) 'Costa Ricas Nationalparks: belagerte Insein. Tourismus als ökologische Chance und Gefahr' Nr 146: p5.

Neue Zürcher Zeitung (1992) 'Süss-saure Bananen für Costa Rica' Nr 152: p5.

Neue Zürcher Zeitung (1995) 'Kohlenstoffbindung in Costa Ricas Wäldern. Finanzierung durch Swaps amerikanischer Luftverschmutzer?' Nr 66: p5.

Opler, P A & Janzen, D H (1983) 'Cordia Alliodora (Laurel)' in Janzen, D H *Costa Rican Natural History* pp219–221. Chicago: University of Chicago Press.

Pedroni, L & Flores Rodas, J (1992) *Diagnostico Forestal Regional para Centro America y Propuestas de Trabajo*. Bern: Intercooperation.

Sayer, J, McNeely, J A & Stuart, S N (1990) 'The Conservation of Tropical Forest Vertebrates' in Peters, G & Hutterer, R *Vertebrates in the Tropics*, pp407–419. Bonn: Museum Alexander Koenig.

Stadtmüller, T & Aus der Beek, R (1992) *Development of Forest Management Techniques for Tropical High Mountain Primary Oak-Bamboo Forest*. Proceedings of the Oxford Conference on Tropical Forests, Voluntary Paper. Oxford.

The Tico Times (1990) 'Landless Farmers Threaten Remaining Forests' 30 March: p11.

Uhl, C, Buschbacher, R & Serrão, E A S (1988) 'Abandoned Pastures in Eastern Amazonia. 1. Patterns of Plan Succession' *Journal of Ecology*, 76: pp663–681.

Utting, P (1993) *Trees, People and Power. Social Dimensions of Deforestation and Forest Protection in Central America*. London: Earthscan.

Veillon, J-P (1976) 'Las Deforestaciones en los Llanos Occidentales de Venezuela desde 1950 hasta 1975' in Hamilton, L S, Steyermark, J, Veillon, J-P & Mondolfi, E *Conservacion de los Bosques Humedos de Venezuela*. Caracas: Sierra Club.

Veillon, J-P (191) *Los Bosques Naturales de Venezuela. Parte II: Los bosques xerófilos*. Mérida: Universidad de los Andes, Instituto de Silvicultura.

Veillon, J-P (1992) *Los Bosques Naturales de Venezuela. Parte III: Los bosques tropéofitos*. Mérida: Universidad de los Andes, Instituto de Silvicultura.

Weidelt, H-J (1993) 'Some Effects of Selective Logging on Forest Productivity and Ecology' in Leith, H & Lohmann, M *Restoration of Tropical Forest Ecosystems*. Amsterdam: Kluwer.

Chapter 7: Indonesia

1. Cf. Torquebiau, 1984.
2. Mary and Michon, 1987, p. 52; Michon and Jafarsidik, 1989, p. 63.
3. Jackfruit: *Artocarpus heterophyllus*; kalong: *Pteropus vampyrus*.
4. Mary and Michon, 1987; p. 51.
5. Durian: *Durio zibethinus*; Duku: *Lansium domesticum*.
6. de Foresta and Michon, 1994; p. 13; Sayer, 1995, p. 13.
7. Cleary and Eaton, 1992; p. 94.
8. Cf. Colfer, 1992; p. 73.
9. Dove, 1983; p. 86.
10. Dove, 1983; p. 91.
11. Potter, 1988; p. 129.
12. Dove, 1985; p. 2.
13. Gillis, 1988; p. 49.
14. Cf. Nair, 1993 p. 68 ff.
15. Cf. Peluso, 1993.
16. *Shorea macrophylla, S. seminis* and *S. splendida*; see Whitmore, 1975; p. 187.
17. Dove, 1993; p. 117.
18. Jacobs, 1988; pp. 202; 225.
19. Dove, 1983; p. 94.
20. *Eusideroxylon zwageri*.
21. Potter, 1988; p. 136.
22. Ibid., p. 144.
23. Peluso, 1993; p. 6.
24. Küchli, 1982; p. 36; *Tages Anzeiger*, 14 September, 1989.
25. Manning, 1971, p. 43; Küchli, 1982, p. 36.
26. Gillis, 1988, p. 50.
27. Brookfield, Lian, Kwai-Sim and Potter, 1990, p. 500.
28. *Tages Anzeiger*, 21 April, 1990.
29. Cf. Johnson and Dykstra, 1978.
30. Weidelt, 1986, p. 23a.
31. Gillis, 1988, p. 50; Cleary and Eaton, 1992, p. 142.
32. Gillis, 1988, p. 56.
33. Ibid., p. 77.
34. Cf. Cleary and Eaton, 1992, p. 228.
35. Cf. Jacobs, 1988, p. 229.
36. Huss and Sutisna, 1993, p. 147.
37. Garrity and Khan, 1994, p. 28.
38. Cf. Inoue and Lahjie, 1990.
39. Gillis, 1988, p. 48.
40. Inoue and Lahjie, 1990, p. 282.
41. Cf. Colfer, 1982.
42. Peluso, 1993, p. 68.
43. Cf. Colchester, 1992, p. 8.
44. Cf. *Time*, 1992.
45. Barber, Johnson and Hafild, 1994, p. 70–71.
46. Cf. Cleary and Eaton, 1992, p. 145; Brookfield, Lian, Kwai-Sim and Potter, 1990, p. 503.
47. Barber, Johnson and Hafild, 1994, p. 41.
48. Colfer, 1992, p. 81.
49. Barber, Johnson and Hafild, 1994, p. 22.
50. Brookfield, Lian, Kwai-Sim and Potter, 1990, p. 503.
51. Repetto, 1990, p., 19.
52. Goodland, Asibey, Post and Dyson, 1991, p. 505.
53. Barber, Johnson and Hafild, 1994, pp. 47, 43.
54. Dove, 1985, p. 26.
55. Barber, Johnson and Hafild, 1994, p. 48.
56. Cf. Dudley, Stolton and Jeanrenaud, 1995.
57. Barber, Johnson and Hafild, 1994. p. 23.
58. Cf. Michon and de Foresta, 1995.
59. Mary and Michon, 1987, p. 49.
60. de Foresta and Michon, 1994, p. 13.
61. Rehm and Espig, 1984, p. 226.
62. Godoy, 1990, p. 167.
63. Cf. Freese, 1994, p., 19.
64. Michon and de Foresta, 1995, p. 94.
65. *Weltwoche*, 1989, No. 51.
66. Garrity and Khan, 1994, p. 2.
67. Michon and de Foresta, 1995, p. 102.
68. Cf. Colfer, 1992, pp. 75, 82.
69. Bertault, 1991.
70. Bandy, 1994, p. 2.
71. Cf.Hutchinson, 1986; Weidelt, 1993.
72. Huss and Sutisna, 1993, pp. 152-153.
73. Personal communication with Willie Smits, Tropenbos-Kalimantan, 17 April, 1990.
74. Bruenig, 1993, p. 175.
75. Poore and Sayer, 1991, p. 50.
76. Cf. Weidelt, 1986, p. 11; Whitten Damanik, Anwar, and Hisyam, 1987, p. 286.

References

Bandy, D (1994) 'From Indonesia' *Slash and Burn – Update on Alternatives*, 1, 3: p2.

Barber, C V, Johnson, N C & Hafild, E (1994) *Breaking the Logjam: Obstacles to Forest Policy Reform in Indonesia and the United States*. Washington: World Resources Institute.

Bertault, J-G (1991) 'Quand la forêt tropicale s'enflamme' *Bois et Forêts de Tropiques*, No 230: pp5–14.

Brookfield, H, Lian, F J, Kwai-Sim, L & Potter, L (1990) 'Borneo and the Malay peninsula' in Turner, B L et al *The Earth as Transformed by Human Action*. Cambridge: Cambridge University Press.

Bruenig, E F (1993) 'Research and Development Programme for Forestry in Sarawak: A Pilot Model Approach Towards Sustainable Forest Management and Economic Development' in Lieth, H & Lohmann, M *Restoration of Tropical Forest Ecosystems*. Amsterdam: Kluwer.

Cleary, M & Eaton, P (1992) *Borneo: Change and Development*. Singapore: Oxford University Press.

Colchester, M (1992) *Sustaining the Forests: The Community-Based Approach in South and South-East Asia.* Geneva: UNRISD.

Colfer-Pierce, C J (1982) 'Kenyah Dayak Tree Cutting: In Context' in *Interaction Between People and Forests in East Kalimantan.* Washington DC: Indonesia-US Man and the Biosphere Project.

Colfer-Pierce, C J (1992) *Shifting Cultivators of Indonesia: Marauders or Managers of the Forest? Rice Production and Forest Use Among the Uma' Jalan of East Kalimantan.* Rome: FASO.

Dove, M R (1983) 'Theories of Swidden Agriculture and the Political Economy of Ignorance' *Agroforestry Systems*, 1: pp85–99.

Dove, M R (1985) *The Agroecological Mythology of the Javanese and the Political Economy of Indonesia.* East–West Environment and Policy Institute, Reprint No 84 of: Indonesia, No 39, April 1985.

Dove, M R (1993) 'The Responses of Dayak and Bearded Pig to Mast-Fruiting in Kalimantan: An Analysis of Nature-Culture Analogies' in Hladik, C M et al *Tropical Forests, People and Food: Biocultural Interactions and Applications to Development.* UNESCO Man and the Biosphere Series 13. Carnforth, New York: Parthenon.

Dudley, N, Stolton, S & Jeanrenaud, J-P (1995) *Pulp Fact. The Environmental and Social Impacts of the Pulp and Paper Industry.* Gland: WWF.

de Foresta, H & Michon, G (1994) 'Agroforests in Sumatra. Where Ecology meets Economy' *Agroforestry Today*: 6, 4: pp12–13.

Freese, C (1994) *The Commercial, Consumptive Use of Wild Species. Implications for Biodiversity Conservation. Interim Report.* Gland: WWF International.

Garrity, D P & Khan, A (1994) *Alternatives to Slash-and-Burn: a Global Initiative. Summary Report of a Workshop in Indonesia 1993.* Nairobi: International Centre for Research in Agroforestry.

Gillis, M (1988) 'Indonesia: Public Policies, Resource Management, and the Tropical Forest' in Repetto, R & Gillis, M (1988) *Public Policies and the Misuse of Forest Resources.* Cambridge: Cambridge University Press.

Godoy, R (1990) 'The Economics of Traditional Rattan Cultivation' *Agroforestry Systems*, 12: pp163–172.

Goodland, R J A, Asibey, E O A, Post, J C & Dyson, M B (1991) 'Tropical Moist Forest Management: The Urgency of Transition to Sustainability' in Constanza, R *Ecological*

Economics. The Science and Management of Sustainability. New York: Columbia University Press.

Huss, J & Sutsina, M (1993) 'Conversion of Exploited Natural Dipterocarp Forests into Semi-natural Production Forests' in Lieth, H & Lohmann, M *Restoration of Tropical Forest Ecosystems.* Amsterdam: Kluwer.

Hutchinson, I D (1986) 'Improvement Thinning in Natural Tropical Forests: Aspects and Institutionalisation' in Mergen, V *Natural Management of Moist Forests.* New Haven: Yale University.

Inoue, M & Lahjie, A M (1990) 'Dynamics of Swidden Agriculture in East Kalimantan' *Agroforestry Systems*, 12: pp269–284.

Jacobs, M (1988) *The Tropical Rain Forest.* Berlin, New York: Springer.

Johnson, N E & Dykstra, G F (1978) *Maintaining Forest Production in East Kalimantan.* Tropical Forestry Research, ITCI (Weyerhaeuser).

Küchli, C (1980) 'Holznutzungen und Forstwirtschaft in Indonesien' *Schweiz Z Forstwes*, 131, 6: pp539–551.

Küchli, C (1982) 'Feuer und kaltes Geld' *Natur*, München, Juli 1982.

Manning, C (1971) 'The Timber Boom with Special Reference to East Kalimantan' *Bulletin of Indonesian Economic Studies*, 7, 3: pp30–60.

Mary, F & Michon, G (1987) 'When Agroforests Drive Back Natural Forests: A Socio-Economic Analysis of a Rice-Agroforest System in Sumatra' *Agroforestry Systems*, 5: pp27–55.

Michon, G & Jafarsidik, D (1989) '*Shorea javanica* Cultivation in Sumatra – an Original Example of Peasant Forest Management Strategy' in Bruenig, E F & Poker, J *Management of the Tropical Rainforests – Utopia or Chance of Survival? Case Study 5*, pp59–67. Baden-Baden: Nomos.

Michon, G & de Foresta, H (1995) 'The Indonesian Agro-Forest Model' in Halladay, P & Gilmour, D A *Conserving Biodiversity outside Protected Areas.* Gland: IUCN.

Nair, P K R (1983) *The Impact of Environmental Change on Forest Management. A Case Study from West Kalimantan, Indonesia.* Rome: FAO.

Poore, D & Sayer, J (1991) *The Management of Tropical Forest Lands. Ecological Guidelines.* Gland, Switzerland: IUCN.

Potter, L (1988) 'Indigenes and Colonisers: Dutch Forest Policy in South and East Borneo (Kalimantan) 1900 to 1950' in Dargavel, J, Dixon, K & Semple, N *Changing*

Tropical Forests. Historical Perspectives on Today's Challenges in Asia, Australasia and Oceania. Canberra: Centre for Resource and Environmental Studies.

Rehm, S & Espig, G (1984) *Die Kulturpflanzen der Tropen und Subtropen.* Stuttgart: Ulmer.

Repetto, R (1990) 'Deforestation in the Tropics' *Scientific American*, 262, 4: pp18–24

Tages-Anzeiger (1989) 'Sie pflegen das Gärtchen und verholzen den Tropenwald – die Japaner und ihr Umweltschutz' 14 September 1989, p2.

Tages-Anzeiger (1990) '"Tag der Erde" endlich auch in Japan begangen. Die angeprangert' 21 April 1990, p2.

Time (1992) 'Empire of the Sons – and Daughters' 3 February 1992, pp20–25.

Torquebiau, E (1984) 'Man-Made Dipterocarp Forest in Sumatra' *Agroforestry Systems*, 2, 2: pp103–127.

Weidelt, H-J (1986) 'Die Auswirkungen waldbaulicher Pflegemassnahmen auf die Entwicklung exploitierter Dipterocarpaceen-Wälder' *Göttinger Beiträge zur Land-und Forstwirtschaft in den Tropen und Subtropen*, Heft 19.

Weidelt, H-J (1993) 'Some Effects of Selective Logging on Forest Productivity and Ecology' in Lieth, H & Lohmann, M *Restoration of Tropical Forest Ecosystems.* Amsterdam: Kluwer.

Weltwoche (1989) 'Die Kunst, den Regenwald zu nutzen und zu schützen. Indonesien auf der Suche nach dem Ausgleich zwischen ökonomischem Wachstum und ökologischer Verantwortung' Nr 51, pp24–25.

Whitmore, T C (1975) *Tropical Rain Forests of the Far East.* Oxford: Clarendon Press.

Whitten, A J, Damanik, J A, Anwar, J & Hisyam, N (1987) *The Ecology of Sumatra.* Yogyakarta: Gadjah Mada University Press.

Chapter 8: Brazil

1   Subler and Uhl, 1990, p. 154; Jordan, 1991, p. 169.
2   Anonymous, 1967.
3   *Platymiscium* sp. (*Leguminosae*).
4   *Erythrina peoppigiana*; cf. Subler and Uhl, 1990, p. 160.
5   Subler and Uhl, 1990, p. 158.
6   *Malpighia* sp.
7   For a discussion of the size of pre-Columbian populations, see Hecht and Cockburn, 1989, p. 9.
8   Roosevelt, 1989, p. 45.
9   Hecht and Cockburn, 1989, p. 30.
10 *Bactris gasipaës*; cf. Balick, 1985. p. 15.
11 *Smilax* spp.
12 Hecht and Cockburn, 1989, p. 61.
13 Cf. Hemming, p. 489.
14 Cf., for instance, Bahri, 1992.
15 Brazil nut (*Bertholletia excelsa*); cf. Mori and Prance, 1990.
16 Cf. Posey, 1985.
17 Balée, 1989, p. 15; Oldeman, 1988, p. 110; McNeely, 1994, p. 12.
18 Lescure and de Castro, 1992, p. 37.
19 Cf. Prance, 1989.
20 Cf. Pinton and Emperaire, 1992, p. 695.
21 Cf. Geffray, 1992.
22 Cf. Collier, 1968.
23 Cf. Santos, 1980, p. 232.
24 Santos, 1980, p. 237, 212.
25 Cf. Goodman, 1988.
26 Hecht and Cockburn, 1989, p. 106.
27 Kohlhepp, 1980, p. 64.
28 Goodman and Hall, 1990, p. 5.
29 Hecht, 1989, p. 231.
30 Hecht, 1992, p. 8; Hecht, 1989, p. 234.
31 Hecht, 1992, p. 15.
32 Cf. Anderson, 1990, p. 9; *Neue Zürcher Zeitung*, 1992, nr. 96; Dorner and Thiesenhusen, 1992, p. 11.
33 Goodman, 1988, p. 43.
34 Goodman, 1988, p. 49.
35 de Souza Martins, 1990, p. 252.
36 Cf. Kohlhepp, 1991, p. 89.
37 Diegues, 1992, p. 7.
38 Goodman and Hall, 1990, p. 9.
39 de Souza Martins, 1990, p. 255.
40 Wagner, 1990, p. 243.
41 Cf. Sawyer, 1990, p. 269.
42 Wagner, 1990, p. 232.
43 Hecht and Cockburn, 1989, p. 168.
44 Cf. Allegretti, 1990, p. 255; Fearnside, 1989b, p. 387.
45 Hecht and Cockburn, 1989, p. 183.
46 Goodman and Hall, 1990, p. 15.
47 Fearnside, 1989b, p. 391.
48 Cf. Brown and Brown, 1992, p. 131.
49 Ibid., p. 132.
50 Schultes, 1980, p. 260.
51 Balick, 1985, p. 341.
52 Cf. Burger, 1991.
53 Fearnside, 1993, p. 541; Castriolo, 1992,

p. 97 quotes the figure 415,215 km^2.
54 Fearnside, personal communication, 27 November, 1993. See also Goodman and Hall, 1990, p. 6.
55 Cf. Fearnside, 1990.
56 Fearnside, 1993, p. 542.
57 Castriolo, 1992, p. 104, 105.
58 Mario Dantas, EMBRAPA Rio Branco, personal communication, 2 December, 1992.
59 Cf. Denich, 1991.
60 Cf. Uhl, Buschbacher and Serrão, 1988.
61 Sawyer, 1990, p. 267.
62 Fearnside, 1989a, p. 61.
63 Cf. Fearnside, 1989a, p. 75; Burger, 1991, p. 90.
64 Cf. Reis Filho, 1992.
65 Hecht and Cockburn, 1989, p. 141.
66 Cf. Barros and Uhl, 1995.

References

Allegretti, M H (1990) 'Extractive Reserves: An Alternative for Reconciling Development and Environmental Conservation in Amazonia' in Anderson, A B (Ed) *Alternatives to Deforestation: Steps Toward Sustainable Use of the Amazon Rain Forest* New York: Columbia University Press.

Anderson, A B (Ed) (1990) *Alternatives to Deforestation: Steps Toward Sustainable Use of the Amazon Rain Forest* New York: Columbia University Press

Anonymous (1967) *Relatos Historicos da Cooperativa Agricola Mista de Tomé Açu Tomé Açu.* CAMTA.

Bahris, S (1992) *L'Agroforesterie, une alternative pour le développement de la plaine alluviale de l'Amazone. L'exemple de l'île de Careiro* Montpellier: Université de Montpellier.

Balée, W (1989) 'The Culture of Amazonian Forests' in Posey, D A & Balée, W *Resource Management in Amazonia: Indigenous and Folk Strategies. Advances in Economic Botany* 7: pp1–21. New York: The New York Botanical Garden.

Balick, M J (1984) 'Ethnobotany in the Neotropics' in Prance, G T & Kallunki, J A *Ethnobotany in the Neotropics. Advances in Economic Botany* 1: pp 9–23. New York: The New York Botanical Garden.

Balick, M J (1985) 'Useful Plants of Amazonia: A Resource of Global Importance' in Prance, G T & Lovejoy, T E *Key Environments: Amazonia.* Oxford: Pergamon Press.

Barros, C & Uhl, C (1995) 'Logging Along the Amazon River and Estuary: Patterns, Problems and Potential' *Forest Ecology and Management* 77: pp87–105.

Brown, Jr, K S, Brown, G G (1992) 'Habitat Alteration and Species Loss in Brazilian Forests' in Whitmore, T C & Sayer, J A *Tropical Deforestation and Species Extinction.* London: Chapman & Hall.

Burger, D (1991) 'Land Use in the Eastern Amazon Region' in Burger, D et al, *Studies on the Utilization and Conservation of Soil in the Eastern Amazon Region.* Eschborn: Deutsche Gesellschaft für Technische Zusammenarbeit (GTZ)

Castriolo de Azambuja, M C (1992) 'The Brazilian Case. Tropical Forest – Victim of Short-Sighted Policy?' in Linder, W (Ed) *Umweltzerstörung und Ressourcenverschwendung, Band 21 der Sozialwissenschaftlichen Studien für das Schweizerische Institut für Auslandsforschung Zürich.* Zürich: Rüegger.

Collier, R (1968) *The River that God Forgot. The Story of the Amazon Rubber Boom.* London: Collins.

Denich, M (1991) 'Vegetation of the Eastern Amazon region with Emphasis on the Vegetation Influenced by Man' in Burger, D et al, *Studies on the Utilization and Conservation of Soil in the Eastern Amazon Region.* Eschborn: Deutsche Gesellschaft für Technische Zusammenarbeit (GTZ)

de Souza Martins, J (1990) 'The Political Impasses of Rural Social Movements in Amazonia' in Goodman, D & Hall, A, *The Future of Amazonia. Destruction or Sustainable Development?* London: Macmillan.

Diegues, C (1992) *The Social Dynamics of Deforestation in the Brazilian Amazon.* Geneva: UNRISD.

Dorner, P & Thiesenhusen, W C (1992) *Land Tenure and Deforestation: Interaction and Environmental Implications.* Geneva: UNRISD.

Fearnside, Ph M (1989a) 'Forest Management in Amazonia: the Need for New Criteria in Evaluating Development Options' *Forest Ecology and Management*, 27: pp61–79.

Fearnside, Ph M (1989b) 'Extractive Reserves in Brazilian Amazonia. An Opportunity to Maintain Tropical Rain Forest Under Sustainable Use' *BioScience* 39 (6): pp387–393.

Fearnside, Ph M (1990) 'The Rate and Extent of Deforestation in Brazilian Amazonia' *Environment Conservation* 17 (3): pp213–225.

Fearnside, Ph M (1993) 'Deforestation in Brazilian Amazonia: The Effect of Population and Land Tenure' *Ambio* 22, 8: pp537–545.

Geffray, Chr (1992) 'La dette imaginaire des collecteurs de caoutchouc' *Cah Sci Hum* 28 (4): pp 705–725.

Goodman, D (1988) 'Agricultural Modernisation, Market Segmentation and Rural Social Structures in Brazil' in Banck, G & Koonings, K *Social Change in Contemporary Brazil*. Amsterdam: CEDLA Latin American Studies 43.

Goodman, D & Hall, A (1990) *The Future of Amazonia, Destruction or Sustainable Development?* London: Macmillan.

Hecht, S B (1989) 'The Sacred Cow in the Green Hell: Livestock and Forest Conversion in the Brazilian Amazon' *The Ecologist* 19 (6): pp229–234.

Hecht, S & Cockburn, A (1989) *The Fate of the Forest. Developers, Destroyers and Defenders of the Amazon*. London, New York: Verso.

Hecht, S B (1992) 'The Logics of Livestock and Deforestation: The Case of Amazonia' in Downing, T E et al (Ed) *Development or Destruction. The Conversion of Tropical Forests to Pasture in Latin America*. Boulder: Westview Press.

Hemming, J (1978) *Red Gold. The Conquest of the Brazilian Indians*. Cambridge: Harvard University Press.

Jordan, C F (1991) 'Nutrient Cycling Processes and Tropical Forest Management' in Gomez-Pompa, A, Withmore, T C & Hadley, M (1991) *Rain Forest Regeneration and Management. Man and the Biosphere Series* Vol 8. Paris: UNESCO.

Kohlhepp, G (1980) 'Analysis of State and Private Regional Development Projects in the Brazilian Amazon Basin' *Applied Geography and Development* 16: pp53–79.

Kohlhepp, G (1991) 'The Destruction of the Tropical Rain Forests in the Amazon Region of Brazil – an Analysis of the Causes and the Current Situation' *Applied Geography and Development* 38: pp87–109.

Lescure, J-P & de Castro, A (1992) 'L'extractivisme en Amazonie centrale. Aperçu des aspects économiques et botaniques' *Bois et forêts des Tropiques* Nr 231: pp35–51.

McNeely, J A (1994) *Coping with Change. People, Forests and Biodiversity*. Gland: IUCN.

Mori, S A & Prance, G T (1990) *Taxonomy, Ecology and Economic Botany of the Brazil Nut (Bertholletia excelsa). Advances in Economic Botany* 8: pp130–150. New York: The New York Botanical Garden.

Neue Zürcher Zeitung (1992) 'Brasiliens Umweltkrise und der Gipfel von Rio. Das Auseinanderklaffen von Wort und Tat' 96: p7.

Oldemand, R A A (1988) 'Tropical America' in Jacobs, M P *The Tropical Rain Forest*. Berlin, New York: Springer.

Pinton, F & Emperaire, L (1992) 'L'extractivisme en Amazonie brésilienne: Un système en crise d'identité' *Cah Sci Hum* 28: pp685–703.

Posey, D A (1985) 'Indigenous management of tropical forest ecosystems: the case of the Kayapó indians of the Brazil Amazon' *Agroforestry Systems* 3: pp139–158.

Prance, G T (1989) *White Gold, The Diary of a Rubber Cutter in the Amazon 1906–1916, by John C Yungjohann*. Oracle: Synergetic Press.

Reis Filho, O (1992) *Photomicrogap-Acre Understory Harvesting System* Rio Branco: Eigenverlag.

Roosevelt, A (1989) 'Resource Management in Amazonia before the Conquest: Beyond Ethnographic Projection' in Posey, D A & Balée, W *Resource Management in Amazonia: Indigenous and Folk Strategies. Advances in Economic Botany* 7: pp1–21. New York: The New York Botanical garden.

Santos, R (1980) *História Econômica da Amazônia (1800–1920)*. São Paulo: Quieroz.

Sawyer, D (1990) 'The Future of Deforestation in Amazonia: A Socioeconomic and Political Analysis' in Anderson, A B (Ed) *Alternatives to Deforestation: Steps Toward Sustainable Use of the Amazon Rain Forest*. New York: Columbia University Press.

Schultes, R E (1980) 'The Amazonia as a Source of New Economic Plants' *Economic Botany*, 33: pp259–266.

Subler, S & Uhl, Chr (1990) 'Japanese Agroforestry in Amazonia' in Anderson, A B (Ed) *Alternatives to Deforestation: Steps Toward Sustainable Use of the Amazon Rain Forest*. New York: Columbia University Press.

Uhl, C, Buschbacher, R & Serrão, E A S (1988) 'Abandoned pastures in Eastern Amazonia. 1. Patterns of Plant Succession' *Journal of Ecology*, 76: pp663–681.

Wagner Berno de Almeida, A (1990) 'The State and Land Conflicts in Amazonia 1964–1988' in Goodman, D & Hall, A *The Future of Amazonia. Destruction or Sustainable Development?* London: Macmillan.

Chapter 9: Thailand

1   See R. Campbell, *Teak-Wallah. The adventures of a young Englishman in Thailand in the 1920s* (Oxford).
2   Latham, 1954, p. 504.
3   Cf. Ramitanondh, 1985.
4   Nair, 1993, p. 4.
5   Ramitanondh, 1985.
6   Sricharatchanya, 1987.
7   Cf. Ramitanondh, 1985.
8   Kanwanich, 1987; Sricharatchanya, 1987; Callister, 1992, p. 71.
9   Cf. Callister, 1992, p. 43.
10 Callister, 1992, p. 70.
11 *Neue Zürcher Zeitung*, 1995, Nr., 192.
12 Boonkird, 1984.
13 Hufschmid, 1994.
14 Personal conversation with Amnuay Corvanich, 18 November, 1987.
15 Cf. Arbhabhirama, 1987.
16 Leungaramsri and Rajesh, 1992, p. 70.
17 Ibid., p. 178.
18 Cf. Küchli, 1990.
19 Wittayapak, 1996, p. 7.
20 Erni, 1996.
21 Lynch and Talbott, 1995, p. 10.
22 Leungaramsri and Rajesh, 1992, pl 57.
23 Lohmann, 1990, p. 13.
24 Wittayapak, 1996, p. 8.

References

Arbhabhirama, A et al (1987) *Thailand Natural Resources Profile*. Bangkok: Thailand Development Research Institute and National Environment Board.

Boonkird, S-A et al (1984) 'Forest villages: an agroforestry approach to rehabilitating forest land degraded by shifting cultivation in Thailand.' *Agroforestry Systems*, 2: pp87–102.

Callister, D J (1992) *Illegal Tropical Timber Trade: Asia-Pacific*. Cambridge: Traffic International.

Campbell, R (1986) *Teak-Wallah. The Adventures of a Young Englishman in Thailand in the 1920s*. Singapore: Oxford University Press.

Erni, Ch (1996) 'Neuer Plan zum Schutz von thailands Wäldern' *Neue Zürcher Zeitung*, Nr 76: p7.

Hufschmid, P H (1994) 'Ein Fall von Entwicklungshilfe' *Zürich: Tages-Anzeiger*, 2 March 1994.

Kanwanich, S (1987) '"Dark forces" killing forests' *Bangkok Post*, 15 May 1987.

Küchli, C (1990) 'Teak, Tapioka und die Walddörfer in thailand' *Schwiez Z Forstwes*, 141, 6: pp463–477.

Latham, B (1954) 'The growth of the teak trade' *Wood*, 19: pp371–373; 415–417; 451–453; 504–506.

Leungaramsri, P & Rajesh, N (1992) *The Future of People and Forests in Thailand after the Logging Ban*. Bangkok: Project for Ecological Recovery.

Lohmann, L (1990) 'Commercial Tree Plantations in Thailand: Deforestation by Any Other Name' *The Ecologist*, 20, 1: pp–17.

Lynch, O J & Talbott, K (1995) *Balancing Acts: Community-Based Forest Management and National Law in Asia and the Pacific*. Washington: World Resources Institute.

Nair, P K R (1993) *An Introduction to Agroforestry*. Dordrecht: Kluwer Academic Publishers.

Nartsupha, C (1986) 'The village economy in pre-capitalist Thailand' in Phongphit, S (Ed) *Back to the Roots. Village and Self-Reliance in a Thai Context*. Bangkok: Rural Development Documentation Centre (RUDOC).

Neue Zürcher Zeitung (1995) 'Raubbau an Kambodschas Wäldern' Nr 192, p5.

Ramitanondh, S (1985) 'Socio-economic Benefits from Social Forestry: for Whom? (The Case of Northern Thailand)' in Rao, Y S et al *Community Forestry: Socio-economic Aspects*. Bangkok: RAPA (FAO).

Sricharatchanya, P (1987) 'Jungle Warfare' *Far Eastern Economic Review*, 17 September 1987.

Wittayapak, C (1996) 'Forestry without Legal Bases: Thailand's Experience' *The Common Property Resource Digest* No 38: pp7–8.

Chapter 10: The People's Republic of China

1   Richardson, 1990, p. 274.
2   Shu-Chun, 1927, p. 565.
3   Ibid. p. 568.
4   Menzies, 1992, p. 68.
5   Needham, 1971, p. 244.
6   Lu Zan Shao, personal communication.
7   Menzies, 1992, p. 74.
8   Wang Zhonghan, personal communication.
9   Zhou Hong, personal communication.
10 Vegetative propagation is an asexual form of reproduction by cuttings, in contrast to reproduction with seeds, which results in plants with a new genetic combination.
11 Zhou Hong, personal communication.
12 Scheuch and Scheuch, 1987, p. 40.
13 Ministry of Forestry, 1992, p. 7.
14 Ministry of Forestry, 1992, p. 8.
15 peashrub: *Caragana* spp.
16 Ministry of Forestry, 1986, p. 8.
17 Ministry of Forestry, 1992, p. 14.
18 Ministry of Forestry, 1986, p. 7.
19 Yang Yuchou, Ministry of Forestry, Beijing, personal communication; Richardson, 1990, p. 281.
20 Weisgerber, 1991, p. 1716.
21 Karner and Weisgerber, 1988, p. 2.
22 Ibid. p. 15.
23 *Time*, 10 May, 1993, p. 20; Smil, 1996, p. 24.
24 Weisgerber, 1991, p. 1698.
25 Klyszcz, 1990, p., 19.
26 Ministry of Forestry, 1992, p. 2.
27 Ministry of Forestry, 1992, p. 3.
28 Cf. Ministry of Forestry, 1992.
29 Ministry of Forestry, 1992, p. 14.
30 Ministry of Forestry, 1992, p. 18.
31 Qin Fengzhu, 1986, p. 13.

References

Karner, L & Weisgerber, H (1988) *Chinesisch-deutsches Aufforstungsprojekt Jinshatan, Provinz Shanxi*. Eschborn: GTZ.

Klyszcz, G (1990) *Die Einbindung der örtlichen Bevölkerung (Social Forestry) ist eingeleitet*. Eschborn: GTZ PN 82.2021.2 - 03.200.

Menzies, N K (1992) 'Sources of Demand and Cycles of Logging in Pre-Modern China' in Dargavel, J & Tucker, R (Ed) *Changing Pacific Forests. Historical Perspectives on Forest Economy of the Pacific Basin*. Proceedings of conference sponsored by the Forest History Society and IUFRD, Forest History Group. Durham, NC.

Ministry of Forestry, Bureau of the 'Three North' Protection Forest System (1986) *Work on the Project of 'Three North' Protection Forest System is Underway*. Beijing: Ministry of Forestry.

Ministry of Forestry of the People's Republic of China (1992) *Forestry Development and Environmental Protection in China*. Beijing: Ministry of Forestry.

Needham, J (1971) *Science and Civilisation in China*, Vol 4. Cambridge: Cambridge University Press.

Richardson, S D (1990) *Forests and Forestry in China*. Washington: Island Press.

Qin Fengzhu (1986) 'Forestry for Rural Development: China' in *Five Perspectives on Forestry for Rural Development in the Asia-Pacific Region*. Bangkok: FAO, Regional Office for Asia and the Pacific (RAPA).

Scheuch, E K & Scheuch, U (1987) *China und Indien. Eine soziologische Landvermessung*. Zürich: Interfron.

Shu-Chun, Teng (1927) 'The Early History of Forestry in China' *Journal of Forestry*, 25: pp564–570.

Smil, V (1994) 'Raubzug auf letzte Ressourcen' *NZZ Folio*, 11: pp24–28.

Time, 10 May 1993.

Weisgerber, H (1991) 'Forstliche Verhältnisse in der Volksrepublik China. Erste Ergebnisse deutsch-chinesischer Zusammenarbeit zur Weiderbewaldung des Landes' *Holz-Zentralblatt*, 117: pp1696–1698; pp1716–1718.

Chapter 11: United States

1   Balls, 1962, p. 59.
2   Cf. Ulrich, 1984.
3   *Seedling News*, 1994, p. 4.
4   Moll and Gangloff, 1987, p. 45.
5   Pagel, 1983, p. 26.
6   Ibid., p. 25.
7   Cf. *TreePeople*, 1990, p. 4.
8   Jacobson, 1977, p. 164.
9   Miller and McBride, 1989, p. 66.
10 Cf. Grulke and Miller, 1994.

References

Balls, E K (1962) *Early Uses of California Plants*. Berkeley: University of California Press.

Grulke, N E & Miller, P R (1994) 'Changes in gas exchange characteristics during the life span of giant sequoia: implications for response to current and future concentration of atmospheric ozone' *Tree Physiology* 14: pp659–668.

Jacobson, J S (1977) *The Effects of Photochemical Oxidants on Vegetation*. VDI-Berichte 270 (1977).

Los Angeles Times (1987) 'LA Gangs: Throat of a Nightmare' 9 December 1987, part II, p7.

Miller, P R & McBride, J R (1989) 'Trends of ozone damage to conifer forests in the Western United States, particularly Southern California' in Nutcher, J B & Bucher-Wallin, I *Air Pollution and Forest Decline*, pp61–68. Birmensdorf: WSL.

Moll, G & Gangloff, D (1987) 'Urban Forestry in the United States' *Unasylva*, 39, 1: pp36–45.

Pagel, A A (1983) 'Urban Relief: A Million Trees for Los Angeles' *American Forests*, March 1983.

Seedling News (1994) 'Edison Plants Geo's 200,000th Tree' 16: pp1,4.

TreePeople with Andy and Katie Lipkis (1990) *The Simple Act of Planting a Tree. A Citizen Forester's Guide*. Los Angeles: Tarcher.

Ulrich, R (1984) 'View through a Window May Influence Recovery from Surgery' *Science*, 224: pp420–421.

Chapter 12: Germany

1   Schmidtke, 1981, p. 9.
2   Cf. Maier, 1958, p. 217.
3   Lowood, 1991, p. 318.
4   Schrempp, 1988; Wiemer, 1988.
5   Cf. Volk, 1969, p. 39.
6   Abetz, 1955, p. 187.
7   Cf. Gürth, 1982, p. 33.
8   Scheifele, 1995, p. 235 ff.
9   Hasel, 1985, p. 177.
10 Cf. Schäfer, 1992; Radkau and Schäfer, 1987.
11 Hasel, 1977, p. 76.
12 Ibid. P. 78.
13 Cf. Hockenjos, 1993 and Hockenjos, 1994.
14 Cf. Biolley, 1990.
15 Gürth, 1982, p. 53.
16 Prange, 1989, p. 585; *Allgemeine Forst Zeitschrift/Der Wald*, 1996, p. 237.
17 Cf. Hockenjos, 1993, p. 215.
18 Mitscherlich, 1953, p. 39.
19 Cf. Küchli, 1992, p. 64 ff.
20 Mitscherlich, 1952, p. 10.
21 Ott, 1996, p. 177.
22 Cf. the *Allgemeine Forst Zeitschrift*, 1995, p. 885.
23 Freiburg Department of Forestry, 1994.

References

Abetz, K (1955) *Bäuerliche Waldwirtschaft*. Hamburg: Parey.

Allgemeine Forst Zeitschrift (1995) 'Wir nehmen unsere Kleinheit nicht genau genug wahr. Baden-Württembergischer Forstverein tagte in Villingen-Schwenningen' 16: pp884–887.

Allgemeine Forst Zeitschrift/Der Wald (1996) 'Biodiversität und nachhaltige Forstwirtschaft' 51, 5: pp236–243.

Biolley, H (1980) 'Oeuvre écrite' *Beih Z Schweiz Forstver*, 66: p458.

Forstdirektion Freiburg (1994) 'Schwarzwälder Tannenholz nach Japan exportiert' *Pressemitteilung*, 20 December 1994.

Gürth, P (1982) 'Bestandesgeschichtliche Untersuchungen im mittleren Schwarzwald' *Schriftenreihe der Badischen Forstlichen Versuchsanstalt*, Band 57.

Hasel, K (1977) 'Auswirkungen der Revolution von 1848 und 1849 auf Wald und Jagd, auf Forstverwaltung und Forstbeamte, insbesondere in Baden' *Schriftenreihe der Badischen Forstlichen Versuchsanstalt*, Band 50.

Hasel, K (1985) *Forstgeschichte*. Hamburg: Parey.

Hockenjos, W (1993) 'Die Wiederentdeckung des Femelwaldes. Auf forstgeschichtlicher Spurensuche im Bücherschrank eines badischen Forstamtes' *Allg Forst- u J Ztg*, 164, 12: pp213–218.

Hockenjos, W (1994) 'Naturgemässe Waldwirtschaft als Ideologie – Ursprung und Hintergründe einer Unterstellung' *Der Dauerwald*, Juli 1994: pp24–33.

Küchli, C (1992) *Wurzein und Visionen – Promenaden durch den Schweizer Wald*. Aarau: AT.

Lowood, H E (1991) 'The Calculating Forester: Quantification, Cameral Science, and the Emergence of Scientific Forestry Management in Germany' in Frängsmyr, T et al *The Quantifying Spirit in the 18th Century*. Berkeley: University of California Press.

Maier, K-E (1958) *Oberwolfach. Die Geschichte einer Schwarzwaldgemeinde im Wolftal*. Oberwolfach: Gemeindekanzlei.

Mitscherlich, G (1952) 'Der Tannen-Fichten-(Buchen)-Plenterwald' *Schriftenreihe der Badischen Forstlichen Versuchsansalt*, Heft 8.

Ott, W (1996) 'Wald und Forstwirtschaft in Baden-Württemberg 1995' *AFZ/Der Wald* 51, 4: pp172–177.

Prange, H (1989) 'Entwicklung des Saatgutherkunftsgedankens' *Allgemeine Forst Zeitschrift*, 24–26: pp585–588.

Radkau, J & Schäfer, I (1987) *Holz. Ein Naturstoff in der Technikgeschichte*. Reinbek: Rowohlt.

Schäfer, I (1992) *'Ein Gespenst geht um' – Politik mit der Holznot in Lippe 1750–1850*. Detmold: Selbstverlag des Naturwissenschaftlichen und Historischen Vereins für das Land Lippe e. V.

Scheifele, M (1995) 'Schwarzwalder Holzkönige als Industriepioniere im 18. Jahrhundert – Lebensbilder aus der Wirtschaftsgeschichte des Nordschwarzwaldes' *Allgemeine Forst – und Jagdzeitung* 166, 12: pp235–241.

Schmidtke, H (1981) *Analyse einer Landschaftveränderung, dargestellt am Beispiel des Wolftales im Mittleren Schwarzwald*. Diplomarbeit, Institut für Landespflege und Weltforstwirtschaft, Universität Freiburg.

Schrempp, O (1988) 'Die Flösserei in Wolfach. Erinnerungen an einen alten Berufsstand' in *Wolfach, schwarzwaldstadt mit Tradition*. Freiburg I. Br.: Rombach.

Volk, H (1969) 'Untersuchungen zur Ausbreitung und künstlichen Einbringung der Fiche im Schwarzwald' *Schriftenreihe Landesforstverwaltung Baden-Württemberg 28*.

Wiemer, K-P (1988) 'Die Flösserei auf Mittel- und Niederrhein im 18. Jahrhundert. in Keweloh, H-W *Auf den spuren der Flösser*. Stuttgart: Theiss.